'Our Accider^t^ ^1^ ^r^ ^,^

Adventure Storie:
Children and the

A male great spotted woodpecker feeding his only fledgling ...
but which is which? Go to the bottom of page XIV for the answer.

Written by Stephen Frye & illustrated by Laura Zwaga

Photography by Stephen Frye

Front cover: *"The Story Teller"* - Black Down Hill

Back cover: *"The flaming red sun was setting early, and the breeze-kissed trees
cast ever-growing shadows across the forest floor that looked like dancing elves or
woodland spirits"* - Lynchmere Common, near Black Down Hill.

**For more photos, updates and events visit the book's
website by Googling "Our Accidental Letters"**

The Preface – For Grownups

Date: 2022

Hello!

Of course, I don't know if you are like me - but if you are, even a little bit, then maybe through lockdown you realised you and your children or grandchildren wanted just a tad more than the usual, rather formulaic children's books about how "Kevin and his kangaroo, Kenny, saved the World" or "When my naughty cousin fell in a pool of sludge". Please don't get me wrong, these types of books are great! But, sometimes it's good to have a change. This book came about quite by chance and was never intended to be published; in fact, it was never intended to be written.

The book is a collection of twelve intimate letters, as if from an uncle or godfather, for the entire family to read and enjoy together. Each is connected to the others and draws the reader and listeners into the natural world, sometimes in our homes or just beyond the front door, no matter where we live. The letters were originally sent to the three children of a family living in south London, starting, quite by accident, just before the coronavirus pandemic took hold. Month by month, the letters snaked through the year and distracted the young family, aged three to nine, from the drudgery of lockdown.

Nature's seasonal regeneration serves as a jumping-off point for the stories, loosely synchronised to the seasons throughout the year, and often, but not always, referring to animal activity in the children's own typical London townhouse garden and local park - in fact, one just like yours. Every animal mentioned, *except for Edward of course,* can now be seen, in "the wild", within forty-five miles of the centre of

London and other big cities or towns.

The intimacy of writing these letters, across both the geographical and generational divide, dovetails with the connection we have with the natural world and emotional experiences we all share. Through past and present adventures and discovery, the stories set out to balance fun, friendship, freedom, excitement and amusing annoyance with loss and sorrow, childhood fears and the ever-changing environment. The book also marks a time of hope as beavers and otters return to our rivers, ravens and white-tailed eagles revisit our skies and salmon migrate, once more, up many of our rivers; sometimes even through or over our towns.

Every story is based on factual events, with a dusting of imagination, and each is accompanied by illustrations, quizzes, surprising "Fun True or False" sections, and family activities for discovering nature in our back yards. There is a map to show where the stories took place, along with access details to the sites where applicable.

To find out why I wrote the first letter you'll have to buy or borrow the book. But, I will say this; the initial letter was an apology ... an act of sheer cowardice.

Now, before you either read on or put this book back on the shelf, I'd like to share with you a tiny but profound experience from my life's index that illustrates just how nature and a little piece of storytelling can bring the generations together. It shouldn't take you long, the story is free, and I'm sure the bookseller won't mind.

'A hidden world in plain sight.'

Many years ago, I was home from work unusually early for my eldest son's sixth birthday party. It was a sunny day in late May, and the celebrations were being held in the small back garden of our three-up, two-down. A little gazebo had been erected and it was festooned with bunting and balloons. There were opened presents aplenty, and wrapping paper lay discarded on the untidy but well-used little lawn. The party table was covered with a brightly coloured tablecloth and decorated with recently spilt orange squash; randomly discarded paper plates; crumpled napkins and partially eaten Birthday cake and sandwiches; all of which was now abandoned for games such as "hide and seek" and "pin the donkey's tail".

As most of the children rushed around the lawn, I noticed one of the boys was lying alone, on his tummy, in a far corner of the garden. He was peering into a patch of slightly longer, unkempt grass. By himself, but quite happy, he'd found something of interest deep within the greenery. I wandered over, unsure if I should interrupt, and knelt down nearby. He seemed to be talking to the grass, but, once he noticed my presence the boy invited me to meet his new friend: a shimmering gold and black ground beetle. I was introduced to the creature, along with a very still woodlouse and several energetic ants. Over the following minutes, he told me the story of their friendship and how the woodlouse had got lost on his way home and was being teased by the ants. He described in detail how he and his friend the beetle had come to the woodlouse's aid. I was encouraged to join in with the occasional observation.

At that moment, I felt a deeply serene and perfect connection between the boy, the gathering of wildlife, and me; all of this amongst the hubbub and mayhem of the party going on around us. I felt truly privileged to have been invited into his secret world.

Without notice, he turned his head towards me, looked quizzically into my eyes, smiled, then jumped up and ran over to his friends to rejoin the party, without another word being spoken.

All that needed to be said had been said.

I gazed back towards the beetle, who looked equally surprised at the boy's departure before he too scampered off, leaving me, a grown man, lying by myself face down on the grass with only the long-dead remains of the woodlouse for company. Even the ants had deserted me as I peered into the foliage once more.

It was only then, I realised a gaggle of mother-helpers was staring at me, mouths open, from the other side of the garden as Bridget, my long-suffering wife, returned from the kitchen with a tray of biscuits, six cups and a pot of Earl Grey. Much to her consternation and somewhat perplexed, she surveyed the situation of me sprawled on the lawn, alone, and still in my work suit and tie. Then, she tilted her head to the left as if musing over a modern sculpture, gave out a long and exasperated sigh - befitting of Sybil Fawlty - and without seeking an explanation, turned away to the gaggle of mums.

"Oh dear…Anyone for Tea?"

All profits from the sale of this book go to Teenage Cancer Trust and the Suffolk Owl Sanctuary

Where conservation comes first

DEDICATIONS AND THANKS

This book is dedicated to:
Bridget & my children; Andrew, Jonathan and Claire
My Grandchildren Violet, Maddie & Bump.

***

With special good wishes to The Gairdner Children
Jemima, William & Camilla, for whom these letters were originally written.

***

And to Holly Dog, my faithful friend and "Listening Editor".

(Courtesy of Tricia Luke)

***

A Special Dedication to "Ned", who helped create our lovely garden and
tragically took his own life, aged just 20 years.

Greatest thanks to Laura Zwaga for illustrating this entire book, without
charge, and Lucy Zwaga for helping Laura set out the draft manuscript

My special thanks to Jon Taylor, my editor for all things relating to the natural
world and Helen Ball for editing this book.

Thanks also to Georgina Fradgley (editor), who gave me her shoulder to cry on,
when trying to get the letters published.

My undying gratitude to Bruce Graham of Night Owl Graphic Design whose
patience and dedication put this book together.

With a special mention for Susan Reynolds, who asked all the right questions of
the narrative, corrected my useless spelling and grammar and gave me "7/10 &
must do better" ... Once a teacher; always a teacher!

FOREWORD

In aid of

FROM LAURA WOODCOCK

The past two years have been difficult for everybody, not least for young people with cancer and the charities that support them. For *Teenage Cancer Trust*, much needed fundraising was put on hold. So, when Stephen contacted us and said that profits from his new children's book, "*Our Accidental Letters*", were coming to the charity and asked us to write this Foreword, I was only too pleased to do so.

Through the old fashioned, but intimate use of letter writing, Stephen has brought the natural world within touching distance of us all; children and grownups alike, and no matter where we live. Writing to a young family in south west London, his intimate style and voice combines fact with fantasy, allowing the reader and young listeners to almost smell the wildlife around us, often just at the end of our gardens or local parks.

His letters, no, *our letters* journey through time and across our beautiful land to bring us discovery, and a little adventure, right on our doorstep. The book also marks this point in time when there is a real hope for the regeneration of our countryside and breakthroughs in children's cancer treatment, all set within these difficult times.

Like me, Stephen's love of nature shines through many of the bedtime stories and left me wanting more.

All the best and thanks for supporting Teenage Cancer Trust,

Laura Woodcock
Head of Community Fundraising

The Introductory Letter –
For Grownups (& Kids)

"Genius, pure genius," I now realised why I'd married her.'

Date: November.

Dear All

When my own children were young, Bridget, my long-suffering wife, would read them classic children's stories when they were ready for bed. I, on the other hand, would *tell* them tales that I made up, often as I went along. These stories were set in a magical countryside, encompassing forests and fields of complete fantasy. On reflection, I regretted not basing the stories on events and places I'd actually experienced, but thought no more of it.

Twenty-five years later, I was given the chance to put that right, quite by accident.

I've been prone to exaggeration when recalling stories for children; well, after all, I am a fisherman. On one occasion, I was demonstrating my great age and wisdom by telling the children I had *"helped with the construction of Stonehenge."* I *forgot* to reveal that my limited involvement had been restricted to lightly scratching my initials into the lichen on one of the outer ring's ancient stones, some 56 years ago, aged 7.

Likewise, I should be forgiven for firing the imagination of children beyond practical expectations by suggesting and helping to plan a camping trip ... *To the Moon.*

This is all very well when it was my own children, as I, and my exasperated wife, had to live with the fallout and disappointment when such trips had to be cancelled due to "operational reasons". A mere detail, in my way of looking at life.

It's a very different matter building expectations in other people's children; which is exactly what happened on 21st August 2019, when "Auntie" Bridget and I attended the Hythe *Venetian Fete* in Kent with the extended family of Bridget's goddaughter, Emma. This floating carnival takes place on Hythe's Royal Military Canal, is held once every two years, and I thoroughly recommend it. Each float tells a story or relives an historic event. All are illuminated for the evening parade and manned by grownups and children dressed in appropriate costumes.

As the sun was setting, we met the excited young family next to a two-wheeled market stall barrow. It was beautifully painted in dark red with green swirly writing, just like a billboard at a circus. The top was flat, with a raised edge, and about the size of a beach towel. In the centre sat a circular cauldron, and in the middle of that lived "the web-maker"; a mechanical, supercharged "spider". At the command of the ringmaster, and after being fed with sugar, rather than a diet of bugs, the spider spun around and around, creating its fine pink web ... not to catch a fly, but to catch a child. Long sticks were thrust into the sugary threads before the web and sticks were pulled out and presented to the waiting children by a tubby clown.

With candyfloss in hand, we bustled our way past jolly stalls selling everything from cushions to cuddly toys, hot dogs to hamburgers, until we reached the top of the bank overlooking the glistening water of the canal. Sidestepping down the grassy slope, we arrived within touching distance of the water's edge. There, we made ourselves comfortable in preparation for the start of the parade on temporary wooden benches, under one of many oak trees festooned with trails of coloured lights and bunting to create a magical, shadowy atmosphere.

As the evening procession of brightly lit and decorated floats began to drift pass, I just happened to remark to Emma's three children, aged between three and nine, what fun it would be if we collectively built our *own* float for entry in the next Venetian Fete, to be held in 2021. This was met with understandable excitement from the children, which was only matched by the consternation of "Auntie" B and the children's parents and grandparents.

Anyway, detailed plans were drawn up for a float theme, along with outline designs and our individual roles; all this as we watched the illuminated cavalcade pass by on the canal. I simply added fuel to the fire of enthusiasm at the appropriate moments with the occasional "helpful" suggestion and additional technical support to launch our adventure.

As the carnival ended, we said our goodbyes and parted company from the family.

Now, the best thing about being a Great Godparent, in both senses of the word *"great"*, is that you just walk away from events such as this without a care in the world; get in the car and drive home; think no more about it, just reflect on what a fabulous evening you've just had.

Well, life's just not that easy, is it? Some weeks later, Bridget was having a natter with her old friend Jane, grandmother to the three children, when it came up in the conversation that Jemima, the eldest grandchild, had been busily making more detailed plans for "Our Carnival Float Adventure." Furthermore, she had enlisted half of her class at school to make the float and the other half to "man it", as the project had progressed in my absence.

I don't need to humiliate myself by recalling the exact details of the telling-off I received just after Bridget put the phone down from her friend. However, I'm prepared to say a somewhat one-sided agreement was reached. I was *ordered* to contact the three children and explain *why* we would be unable to enter a float into the 2021 fete procession.

'How am I going to do that?' I pleaded with my wife.

I précis her reply in polite, if not altogether accurate, language:

'That's your problem, *Matey*!'

I set about composing a telephone call:

'Hello, is that Jemima? …. Bit of bad news, I'm afraid, about the Venetian Fete … See, Errr, it's been called off, due to a … terrible earthquake'.

Or:

'Hi William. Thanks for the snake's skin you found and gave to me for safekeeping ... Oh, and by the way, next year's Venetian Fete has had to be cancelled because the canal's dried up due to an enormous leak.'

I ran these promising storylines past my other half, who, with hands on hips was able, almost calmly, to explain the pitfalls of this approach. It all seemed perfectly reasonable to me, but there again it would, wouldn't it.

'An apology letter, that's what you're going to send. And, whilst you're at it, why not sugar the pill with one of your stories,' directed Auntie B.

'*Genius - pure genius*!' I now realised why I'd married her.

I could write a grovelling letter of apology; explain why we would be unable to enter a float into the fete, and tell the children about a slightly exaggerated adventure I had had the previous week whilst out walking. Perfect!

Well, the story was short and the apology shorter, but the children said they enjoyed it and I promised to write another … and another … and another as lockdown applied its tragic grip.

So this unintended book started with an *accidental letter.*

Now, whilst I don't have the knowledge to be called a naturalist, I do have an absolute passion for nature, and my stories have a firm foundation built on what I call 'Fisherman's Facts', where reality is stretched only slightly by my imagination. For me, the natural world is not just about animals, plants and landscape; nature also intertwines with our emotions and feelings.

Each story is based solidly on my own observations, and I've allowed myself to bring together elements of several experiences to create a single story. Many of them are exactly as I remember, and I've used this simile to explain the rest: these stories are like sunflowers, firmly planted in the Garden of Fact, but they enjoy peering over the fence and bathing in the radiant light of the utopian Garden of Fiction next-door.

Every letter is genuine, with some of the names, introductions and references, etc. changed, and all were written to be read by a parent, grandparent, or guardian to their charges. But as the letters have been passed around, from family to family, it became clear both children and grownups sometimes read the stories on their own.

***

Kids, before you start to read these letters, I feel I need to give you a tiny insight into our strange natural World and MY way of looking at it.

Firstly, it's great to know just how much you enjoy discovering things about nature and love a good adventure. You may have seen programmes on the television showing faraway expeditions, in which scientists and explorers go to places we can only dream of visiting. But you and I don't have to go further than our own countryside or local parks to find adventure. In fact, we hardly have to leave our homes, to come into contact with interesting wildlife … if only we would look.

Now, I wouldn't be surprised if you found that some animals are a little bit scary and we often don't really know why. Maybe it's because they've got too many legs or no legs at all; maybe we think they might sting or bite; maybe they jump or flutter. But whatever it is, sometimes there's something about them that just doesn't seem quite right. What I do know is that every creature and plant in our gardens, parks and even in our houses has at least one fascinating fact that once known might make us interested enough to find out more about them. Don't believe me? Well, here are two, curious examples. Only a few people actually like hornets, which are a kind of super-sized wasp. Well, I'm one of those people. Did you know hornets are the only member of the British wasp or bee families that can see well enough to fly at night - but only when the moon's shining? So, if you hear a tapping on your bedroom window, late at night, maybe it's a friendly hornet wishing you: "Good night; sleep tight and don't let the bugs bite!"

Secondly, woodpigeons don't feed their newly hatched chicks on seeds, worms, or any other food brought directly from the garden. Nope, they feed them on "pigeon milk" that both parents produce in a kind of stomach called a crop. I don't know about you but I'm not sure I'd want to put their milk on my breakfast cereal!

I would guess you didn't know either of these two facts, but well done if you did!

Nature is a funny old thing. It can make us feel happy and sad; excited and scared; fascinated and frustrated. But the best thing about nature is that we can see it everywhere; outside, inside and even in our bedrooms. What's more, you and I are part of it.

These stories are a mixture of countryside adventures, fun things I've seen around the garden, and the wild outdoors; all brought together by my imagination. A few of the stories can be a little sad and others a touch scary, but that's our natural world for you.

The truth is I never really grew up; I just grew old. So let's travel together from garden to forest; river to moorland; outside and inside. Join me and my faithful companion, Holly Dog, on these daytime and night-time journeys of magical discovery. We'll meet foxes, deer and snakes, ravens, a mystical creature from Exmoor, as well as the killer "Esox Lucius", and many more. And once you've read all the letters they won't be just my stories; they'll be our stories.

I hope you enjoy reading "Our Accidental Letters" as much as I have enjoyed writing them.

With my very best regards,

Stephen Frye
Stephen Frye (Uncle)

Here is the answer to the question, on page I, *which woodpecker is which?* ... the woodpecker on the left is the adult male and the young fledgling is on the right, with the *red cap.*

'Our Accidental Letters'

Adventure Stories in Nature for Children and the Whole Family

Written by Stephen Frye & illustrated by Laura Zwaga

The importance of letters

"To send a letter is a good way to go somewhere, without moving anything but your heart" Phyllis Grissim-Theroux

---

"Nature is a book, a letter, a fairy tale ..." Johann Georg Haman

---

"A visit or phone call brings joy and leaves warm, yet fading memories. But letters; letters are each a gift, capturing the moment forever. And, like a fine wine, the best letters mature with age; though, unlike a fine wine, they can be revisited; read; touched and cherished, time and time again." Stephen Frye

---

OUR ACCIDENTAL LETTERS
THE LETTERS

BLACK DOWN HILL

Lord Tennyson called mysterious Black Down,
"My demon-haunted hill".

The January Letter - "The Apology"

(EXTRACT FROM THE STORY)

"With Holly Dog now barking excitedly, I dropped to my knees for a closer look and I saw these were no ordinary sticks"

The Family

Dear Kids

I hope you are very well, and I'm sure you had a lovely and exciting Christmas.

I have to start by sharing with you a frustrating and annoying bit of news. I wanted so much for us to enter a "float" into the next Venetian fete as promised, but I have to apologise as I'm afraid that can't now happen. Having investigated our options, it won't be possible to get the boats required and decorate them as we would want. But we will try to do something else outdoors in the future. Maybe we could go camping, climb some trees, and have a great adventure of our own.

So, to try and make up a little for this disappointment, I've written a few short stories for us to share together about wild adventures I had when I was your age, and as a grownup. What's more, if we're not able to meet soon, I'll write some additional stories for you. How does that sound?

So, with no further ado, here is the first, very short, adventure that both Holly Dog and I had just a week ago.

"The Mysterious World of Black Down Hill"

Towering above the landscape where I live in
Haslemere is the highest hill in Sussex; a hill
mysteriously called *Black Down*; a place where
ancient, Bronze Age man used to roam and hunt
in the forests for wild animals, at about the same
time in history as the pyramids were constructed, four
thousand years ago. Even now, their presence can still be felt, and
spearheads found in pits and on bank sides. In the past, Black Down
had offered an escape route and hiding place to highwaymen. And
the restless ghosts of three murderers, hanged nearby on makeshift
gallows, still haunt some local country folk.

From its flat sandstone plateau, seven hundred feet above the
surrounding countryside, you can gaze over three different counties.
And on a clear day, the sea is visible, shimmering in the far distance.

Amongst its steep sides hide magical woods, streams and valleys,
and all are blessed with the warmth of sunshine in summer and
cursed with a snowy chill in winter. On the high heathland, and in
the wondrous woodland, roe deer roam free with foxes and badgers,
as well as rare sand lizards, snakes, dragonflies and birds. This is a
hidden and enchanted world, just waiting to be explored.

Four weeks ago, I heard from a close friend that the valleys, on the
far side of Black Down, were soon to have two new, secretive visitors:
a pair of beavers.

Now, beavers live in river homes called "lodges", made from twigs,
sticks, and small trees, which they gather from the nearby woods.
Often they cut down these trees by chewing through the bottom of

Colour me in!

the tree trunks, before pulling them, with their teeth, across the land and into the water to create dams, pools and food stores. Don't you try doing this in your garden or local park!

Well, the other week, just after an early and delicious Sunday lunch made by Auntie Bridget, I listened to the weekend weather report on the radio. The weatherman had a stern voice as he forecasted winter storms to come over the following week.

'From late tonight and into the early morning, snowstorms and strong gales will bring hazardous conditions as well as disruption and damage, especially over high ground,' he warned. 'Our advice is to stay indoors, until further notice'.

I had been impatient to find the beavers since being told of their possible arrival, and I thought this afternoon might have been my last opportunity for an outdoor adventure before the storms rolled in.

Packing a rucksack with provisions, some warm clothing, a head-torch and a cagoule, I set off with my faithful fourteen-year-old Labrador, Holly Dog, to climb the steep and zigzagging path that leads to the sandy heathland summit of Black Down, in search of our new furry friends.

On our way, I called back to Holly Dog: "Come on slowcoach, it gets dark early on these winter nights!" She didn't reply, and kept sniffing each bush we passed by.

The path was rocky and rough; scraped away over hundreds of years by rivulets of rainwater, the hooves of highwaymen's horses, and cattle as they trudged up and down in bygone times, just as Holly Dog and I were doing this winter's afternoon. Either side of the track, higgledy-piggledy hedgerows gave way to rusty brown bracken as the trail narrowed and neared its end.

At the top, I stopped, bent over slightly and leant against a silver birch tree to take a break and catch my breath. After a few seconds, I looked back down the path for Holly Dog, but she was nowhere to be seen.

"Holly Dog, where've you got to?"

Rustlings from a nearby thicket gave away her hiding place. Holly Dog reappeared moments later and slowly made her way to the path just in front of me. She looked nervous and sniffed the chilling air with each step; lifting her outstretched nose a little higher with every intake of breath.

Dogs have a *"sixth sense"* when investigating their surroundings, and can often detect danger and strangeness long before us humans.

'What's up Old Girl, seen a ghost?' I asked as she looked back towards me.

Then, my faithful friend just turned away and continued to sniff the air.

Our pathway flattened out into a woodland of ancient Scots

pine and beech trees. They stood wise and majestic on their hilltop citadel. The forest had witnessed and survived centuries of gales; seen many devastating storms and offered shelter to animals and highwaymen alike.

Beyond the trees, lay an open, bobbly heathland, where wild bilberry bushes jostled for position with faded purple heather and spiteful, spiky, green gorse, just waiting to injure any unwelcome passerby. All this scrubby vegetation offered a little protection to small birds, such as "ticking" wrens and restless Dartford warblers, from attack by flying predators, like buzzards, hovering kestrels and the occasional goshawk.

We followed along one of the narrow rocky, ancient tracks. It looked like the arched, scaly back of a partially buried giant crocodile and was the colour of a cobra, waiting to be awoken as it snaked across this mystical and secret wonderland, high in the sky. From past visits, I had named a few of the paths after animals I'd discovered, such as Adder Alley and Beetle Drive.

From a towering headland to the south, where a prehistoric fort once stood, I looked out over a deep valley onto a patchwork of fields below. A distant farmhouse gently breathed out grey smoke from its chimney. And as the wispy plume rose slowly into the sky, it was welcomed by the final afternoon cry of a lone buzzard, spiralling high above.

'What do you think, Holly Dog? It's beautiful up here, isn't it?' She just sniffed the air once more, and looked out over the distant, darkening fields.

The weather was on the change, and as I stood there, I thought I

Colour me in!

could feel the chill of the fort's warrior spirits
lifting through the air, like the farmhouse smoke,
as if they too were on a twilight journey, halfway to
heaven in the fading, golden light of this winter's day.
As we walked down into a small valley, an impish
north wind flicked its icy fingers down my uncovered
neck, which left me with the uncomfortable feeling
we were being watched. It also reminded me that
snow was on its way. The flaming red sun was setting early, and the
breeze-kissed trees cast ever-growing shadows across the forest floor
that looked like dancing elves or woodland spirits.

I peered up through the high canopy of oak and beech trees, and
saw a tawny owl, preparing for its own night-time adventure.

'Good luck my feathered friend,' I whispered, peering up into the tree.

A little further down the narrowing trail, I heard the noisy rustling
of what I thought might have been a young badger, in a far-off,
tangled thicket.

'Holly Dog, shall we take a look?' She wasn't so sure.

Leaving the path, I crept slowly through the twisted undergrowth
and noticed the world around me had become very quiet and still.
All I could hear were my own footsteps on broken twigs as I felt my
heart pounding with excitement.

Dusk was falling quickly onto the forest when I reached a tiny
clearing in front of the thicket. It was then I saw the slight movement
of a wild animal; or was it the spirit of an ancient woodland hunter,
disappearing behind the intertwined brambles? To be truthful, I'm
not certain exactly what I saw. Could it have been a beaver, making

its way to the safety of the nearby stream, or the stripy young badger I may have heard earlier? Perhaps it might have been a wild boar that had escaped from a nearby farm some years before; or, was it the ghostly presence of a long-dead highwayman?

I crouched a little, and gradually crept around the brambles, making sure I made as little noise as possible, whilst Holly Dog looked on from a distance at my progress. Well, to my disappointment - or was it relief? - there was nothing to be seen, except a patch of flattened bracken, about the size of a large dog's bed.

Now, there seemed to be lots of questions, but not many answers, and to make matters worse, I didn't see any beavers that evening, or any sign of them. "Ah," I can hear you say, "What sort of a story about beavers ends with no beavers?" Well, this one, I guess. And, I can assure you, I too was also a little disappointed. You see, in nature, we often don't find what we're looking for - but the natural world will always come up with unexpected surprises. And so it was, on this chilly winter's evening as I wondered what creature or spirit I'd just seen in the gloom of the clearing.

Then, as I turned to leave, Holly Dog started to growl at something in front of her, which frightened a flock of wood pigeons into flight. I walked over and noticed that nestling in the long grass was, what appeared to be, two sticks.

'Well, old girl, what have you found here then?'

Colour me in!

11

With Holly Dog now barking even more excitedly, I dropped to my knees for a closer look and I saw these were no ordinary sticks but a pair of perfectly matching antlers. Both were rough and bumpy at the bottom but smooth and rounded nearer the three tips on each. At just 15 centimetres long, their curved shape, weight and balance gave me a strange sense of connection when I held them; a feeling that I was actually touching the magnificent animal they once adorned. I realised these antlers weren't just beautiful to look at - they'd been used to fight many a short battle, deep in the woods on the hillsides of Black Down.

'Clever girl! I would have walked right past them'. She wagged her tail as I patted her head.

Although these antlers were shed by their owner some months before, could the animal I'd just seen, disappearing behind the bramble bush, be one and the same creature? Possibly it had been guarding them whilst lying on the bracken bed.

I gazed around and had the feeling I was, again, being watched from the dark shadows of the surrounding trees, but thought no more of it. Slowly I got to my feet and, without a second thought, stuffed both antlers into my backpack for safekeeping, just as snowflakes gently started to drift down through the open canopy of overhead oaks, gathering together like whispering angels as they fell.

The feathery flakes reminded me of a time when I was your age. As a boy, I would excitedly make snowmen and throw snowballs until my hands and feet got so cold they began to hurt. As I stood there, I remembered a game I used to play: looking straight up into the flow of snowflakes, and keeping my eyes wide open, I'd start to count. "One, two, three ..." Whilst counting, I would try to dodge the shimmying clusters of flakes as they fell, this way and that, until one or other of them crashed into either of my open eyes. After the inevitable, but expected shock of the cold snowflake's arrival, the game would restart. Now, half a century later, I just had to have another go. The surprise of the cold snowflake felt just the same as it did all those years ago, and the best I managed was a ten-second count.

'Not bad, for an old fellow. What do you think Holly Dog?' I said, congratulating myself. But, I think I cheated a little by counting rather too quickly, as Holly Dog snorted her disapproval.

The snow had come sooner than forecast. As the cold early evening wrapped around us, and the carpet of white was growing ever more thickly beneath my feet, I realised it was time for Holly Dog and me to leave, but again I had the uneasy feeling of being watched. For a moment, a dark thought flashed through my head. Was I, like the highwaymen of old, stealing the precious antlers from Black Down that didn't belong to me?

'Well, I've got them now,' I said to myself. 'Come on Holly Dog, time for us to go.' But she looked distracted and on edge.

'What's up, have you seen that ghost again?' I joked as she pulled away from me and growled at something in the distant dark.

The snow's magic wand had completely changed the appearance of the landscape that we'd walked through only thirty minutes earlier. And, the unsettling touch of a cold breeze flicked my ears like the teasing of a schoolyard bully.

A hushed winter dreamland was being created around us as Holly Dog and I started retracing our steps through the woods and over a tiny stream on our homeward bound journey.

Half an hour later, we reached the high plateau of Black Down again. The snow was much thicker and falling harder than before, and still I felt we were being followed with each difficult step we took, like prey being stalked by a predator.

An untamed wind was picking up and growled its way through the pine trees, sending piles of snow cascading from the branches above, sometimes hitting both Holly Dog and me as we passed underneath. Paths, once easily followed, disappeared under the white cover, and without the moon to guide us we relied on my old head-torch to light our passage.

Having walked around for what seemed to be hours, I felt as if Black Down had entrapped us, and the storm was becoming increasingly angry. Was the hill enraged because I'd taken not just one but both of the antlers; or were we no longer welcome visitors in this tormented and mystical world of spirits and demons?

I was so relieved when eventually Holly Dog found a long-forgotten and overgrown, gated entrance to a steeply sloping, homeward-bound track.

'Well done Holly Dog. I can always rely on you, my girl.' I congratulated her with a pat.

The ancient trail must have been used hundreds of years ago by the cattle-drovers as they moved their stock up and down the hill throughout the changing seasons. For two kilometres I slipped and tripped as I followed Holly Dog down and down the icy, pebble-strewn path, which nestled between high hedgerows and higher banks. Near the track's end, a fox crossed our path, but it didn't wait for any introductions. He or she simply let out a single yelp and gave us a puzzled look.

'What are you doing here on a night like this?' it seemed to be asking as Holly Dog barked in reply.

Finally, we reached the quieter comfort of the winding country road that led back to a snow-covered Haslemere. I looked up towards Black Down and saw the hill still had much of its rage. I was pleased to be beyond its grasp. Or was I?

On the final bend of our adventure, I was grateful to be welcomed by the lamplight shining out from under our front porch. It lit the perfect beauty of the settled snow in the front garden and also offered Holly Dog and me the promise of safety from the cold and stormy night ahead.

Before going into the house, I took off my damp walking boots, brushed down the snow and dropped the backpack on the right side of the open porch. As I closed the front door on that winter night, I looked out onto the garden and had the strangest feeling of still being watched from the darkest shadows.

'Where have you two been all this time? I was getting worried,' Auntie Bridget said as she met us inside the house.

Later that evening, Holly Dog and I sat by the warmth of the open fire, entranced by the swaying flames that reminded me of the dancing spirit shadows I'd seen on the forest floor of Black Down. Auntie B joined us and I told her about our exciting adventure, but forgetting about the antlers. Then, as the three of us peered silently into the flickering glow of the fire, I remembered I'd put the gifted, *or stolen*, antlers into my backpack. Once more, I felt a little like a thieving highwayman of old for taking these "Black Down treasures" from the forest, and got up to retrieve them from outside the front door.

"Bridget, I've just remembered, I've got something to show you from our adventure. I'll be just a minute, they're in the porch."

"What is it? I'm intrigued," Auntie B asked.

"Ah, you'll have to wait and see."

From the chill of the front step, I could just make out the outline shape of Black Down in the far distance, to my left. The storm and anger seemed to be slipping into the darkness as calm was slowly returning to the great hill. That strange feeling I had had of being watched and hunted was gone, and I felt more at ease as I picked up the rucksack from the left side of the porch. Then, for a moment, I froze, not from the cold, but a peculiar, tingling sensation.

"That's funny! I'm sure I dropped the backpack on the right-hand side of the porch," I whispered to myself, but thought no more of it as I turned towards to the open front door.

Back inside and returning to the cosy fireside, I sat cross-legged on the floor and undid the buckle of the rucksack. Peeking in, I could see my coffee flask, maps, spare jumper and cagoule, but no sign of the antlers. Frantically, I tipped out the contents onto the carpet and gave the backpack an upside-down, violent shake. Urgently, I checked for holes in the rucksack, not believing the antlers had gone. I felt numb, dazed and a little sad at my loss. Then, a cold feeling rippled through me. Had I dreamt about what I'd found? Maybe the antlers never existed, except in my imagination, or only in the magical world of the mysterious Black Down. Had one of the many spirits of the hill reclaimed their treasure, treasure that may not have been mine to take?

'I can't find them! I'm sure I wrapped them in my jumper; right there,' I pointed at the 'empty' pullover.

'Can't find, *what?*' Auntie Bridget quizzed.

'The antlers, of course.'

'Sorry, but what antlers?'

'The antlers I found on Black Down,' I replied, still peering deep into the rucksack.

'I think you're dreaming; the cold's got to your brain. Why didn't you mention them when you got in?' asked Auntie Bridget.

'I just forgot. I swear, they were here ... *right here!*'

I began to have more doubts when Auntie B said: "If they *were* there in the first place, why did you take them? They weren't exactly yours, were they?"

I felt guilty for seizing from nature what wasn't mine; for assuming I had some right to take the antlers. I now recalled in the past, collecting holly sprigs for Christmas decorations, picking bilberries for summer pies and taking logs for winter fires; all without always thinking about the effect it might have on the natural world around me. After all, the bilberries were food for hungry mice; holly berries are eaten by hungrier birds in winter and the logs may have given a safe home for beetles, bugs and snakes in the cold months of the year. I *needed* none of them.

That night I couldn't sleep. Restless and uncomfortable, I got out of bed and moved quietly through the darkness to the chill of the slightly open window and slowly pulled back the curtain. There, in the centre of the snow-covered garden, and in the glistening, dreamy-blue light of the half-moon, stood the ghostly outline of a most magnificent creature. Slowly it became aware of my presence and gradually turned towards me. With its head held high in defiance, I could now see what looked like a crown of velvet-gloved antlers; just the same shape as those I had held earlier. Could they have been the antlers missing from my backpack? No, surely not. The ones I'd taken were bare, without a fleecy covering. Had this animal or phantom come and reclaimed the antlers that were rightfully owned by Black Down?

Slowly the creature turned away, and with great majesty, drifted effortlessly to the moon-shade of the snow-hugged trees at the end of the garden. Then, he disappeared without a sound. Not sure if I was dreaming or awake, I drifted back to bed.

Well, early the next morning, I woke to the racket downstairs of Holly Dog barking at the backdoor. I got up and peered out of the window again, but this time there was no sign of the creature; no footprints in the perfect, deep duvet of crystal snow; no noise ... there were only my silent, peaceful memories of the night before. Or were they just sweet dreams? Mysterious Black Down has ancient, magical powers to play tricks on one's imagination.

Well, that wasn't quite the end of the mystery. Just the other day, when the snow finally thawed, I happened to be clearing up some fallen branches from the garden when Holly Dog started, once again, to bark at something lying amongst a small pile of leaves, near the trees, just as she did on our Black Down adventure. There, as if being presented on nature's cushion of leaves, was not two, but just one forest jewel; *a single antler.*

I felt this was a gift from nature, rather than something I'd just taken without thinking. Why take both antlers when one would do perfectly well to show others?

'It's better to receive from nature, as a gift, what you need, rather than just take everything you want,' I whispered to myself.

Retrieving it from the leaves, I took the antler inside to show Auntie Bridget before giving it pride of place on my specimen table, where it remains to this day.

'See, I told you I wasn't dreaming,' I said to Auntie B, triumphantly; she was unconvinced.

So, maybe when you are next down this way, you could drop in and touch this beautiful object, to see for yourself if you can feel the magic of The Mysterious World of Black Down Hill.

I really hope you enjoyed the story and that it goes, at least, some way to make up for the disappointment of the Venetian Fete. But before I close, I have a question for you: Which animal originally owned the antlers? Could it have been a wild boar; a reindeer; a red deer, or possibly a roe deer? The answer is on the Black Down activities page.

Well, it's time for me to send this letter off to you, but next time we'll journey to a special river and meet two very special friends.

Finest Regards,
Great Old Uncle Steve

OUR ACCIDENTAL LETTERS

For Beaver News see page 213

Holly Dog on Black Down –
"A Cold Winter's Day"

This magnificent young roebuck
stayed in our garden for two days,
his antlers still covered in velvet

With the original letters, I would send a "Gift from Nature".
In this case it was a pair of roe deer antlers. In return I would
receive letters, like this one. *"Our Accidental Letters"*

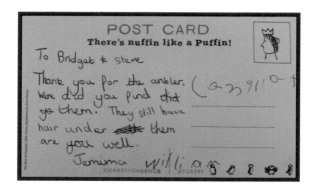

BLACK DOWN ACTIVITIES

The answer to the question – Who did the antlers belong to? ... Is a roebuck (a male roe deer). Did you know, female reindeer are the only female deer in the world to have antlers?

Which ONE of the following "facts" is True?
• Baby beavers, called kits, can't swim until they are, at least three weeks old, when their eyes open.
• The tail of a beaver shrinks in winter.
• Beavers mainly eat leaves, roots, bark and plants, but in winter they also eat fish for fat and protein.
• Generally, the natural colour of a beaver's teeth is light grey.
• Beavers live and have their families inside their river dams for protection.

Mysterious Black Down

See if you can complete the Black Down crossword puzzle below - The answers are at the back of this book

Created using the Crossword Maker on TheTeachersCorner.net

Across
2. What did I tip out of my rucksack?
4. Which animals live in homes called 'lodges'?
7. What breed of dog is Holly dog?
8. What was food for hungry mice?

Down
1. What had escaped from a nearby farm?
3. Where do I live?
5. What fell into my eye?
6. On Black Down, what did Holly dog bark at in the grass?

The answers can be found at the back of the book on page 232

21

MY LITTLE FRIEND

"Come on my friend! It might be the coldest day ever, but I haven't come all this way with breakfast for you to hide in the bushes."

February Letter - "My Little Friend"
(EXTRACT FROM THE STORY)

"I cupped my hands around his cold little body,

then lifted him up and breathed a long, warm

breath over his ruffled feathers"

To The Family

Dear Kids

When I wrote last month, I promised to send you another letter. So here is a story about a little friend I once had. Hopefully, this story will paint for you a picture of our beautiful, chilly winter world in our gardens, parks and countryside. It opens a tiny window on the joy of friendship we might have with both animals and people through our lives, but it also lightly touches on sadness and loss. I hope you enjoy it.

The Robin's Story

Just the other day, I found myself, along with Holly Dog, in the small woods at the top of my garden, cutting and splitting timber to be laid down in crates for next year's fires. It was late afternoon. The day had been grey, angry and accompanied by nasty spitting rain. The clattering branches of the tall beech trees grumbled noisily about the gusty wind.

I too was grumpy, and my fingers were so cold they refused to move when I asked them to. It was then I saw a familiar bird, sheltering amongst the twigs and dead leaves of a fallen branch, which had snapped off two months earlier in an autumn storm. His little red facemask and buttonless waistcoat, tightly zipped to the neck, was puffed out in defiance of the foul weather. So there we were; the trees; the robin; Holly Dog and me, all complaining to each other about the freezing wind and drizzle …. Well, actually *I* was doing most of the complaining and Holly Dog was sniffing around the log store for something to chase, or eat.

After a few minutes, the robin must have thought of something urgent he needed to do before it got too dark and promptly flew off with great urgency to a nearby laurel bush. In that moment, I remembered a time when I once knew of another little robin, and I thought you might like me to share his story with you.

Now, robins are interesting birds, I hope you agree. In the cold weather of winter, their round shape can make each of them look like a jolly Town Crier at a village fete or a Ringmaster at a circus. They can be seen almost everywhere, from tree to bush, and from town to countryside; there is bound to be one near to you right now, if you look hard. Robins are brave little birds. I once saw one peck the tail of a rat … now, that *was* brave! Robins are quite aggressive, spending much of their free time chasing other robins away from what they think is their garden and their garden alone. But they have many qualities; they help to clear our gardens of unwanted bugs and grubs in summer, and bring colour to the garden on a drab winter's morning. All that said, I think their greatest quality is that they are very, *very* good *listeners.*

Let me give you an example: If *you* lie on your back in your garden or a nearby park, looking up at the world of upside-down trees and busy birds flying from branch to branch, you will often be joined by a confident and inquisitive robin. He or she will make you aware of his presence with a couple of chirps to get your attention:

'*Dit ... Dit ... I'm here you know, don't try to ignore me,*' he or she may insist.

Head slanted and with sparkling black eyes, he'll be fixed on your every move. Try to involve him in conversation and he may have only a little to say, but he will always listen. Every now and again, though, his wings will move in a blur of feathers accompanied by a *chirp* or two.

You might hear him or her say: 'Dit, Dit ...Well, I'm still listening, but do you happen to have anything for me to eat? A mealworm or maggot will do *very* nicely.'

At a glance, it's difficult to tell the difference between male and female robins as they look identical, both being dressed in red. However, in spring the males, sometimes called cock robins, sing from high branches, and with heads pointed upwards their beaks look like mini-trumpets. They get very cross if other male robins dare to enter their little patch of garden or woodland.

Young robins, on the other hand, are brown and scruffy. It's as if they've just fallen out of bed, forgotten to brush their hair, or put on their red jumpers before heading off to school. In short, compared to their parents, they are dull little brown speckled birds. Generally, robins don't live beyond their first season, but they can live for over ten years …. I've heard of one living for 18 years!

My Little Friend

Well, enough about robins in general - this is a story about one little robin who was very special to me. I called him "My Little Friend"… Not very catchy I know, but that's who he was to me … *My Little Friend.* It was curious that we formed a friendship at all, as we lived over 70 miles apart and saw each other only a few times a year. He lived on the bankside of the river Wylye in Wiltshire, and I, in the town of Haslemere.

In any case, friends we were; and friendship we had.

We would always meet at the same place and more or less at the same time of day. He never seemed surprised to see me, almost as if he'd been told of my arrival.

Now you may be thinking, how did I know it was the same robin each time we met? And that would be a very good question for you to ask. After all, I have already said: "All robins look the same." Well, it's not *quite* true. If you look carefully, and I mean *very* carefully at robins in your garden or local park, you may notice little differences; a lighter patch of feathers behind his or her head; a flash of white along the edge of a wing; a slightly longer length or different shape of his or her red waistcoat.

I could tell My Little Friend apart from any other robin because, unusually, he had a thin smudge of white feathers running down the left side of his red chest, as if he had spilt milk or paint on his otherwise perfect waistcoat.

Over many years, we met to catch up with each other's news, put the world to rights and complain about the weather before I set off on my riverbank adventures; and he went about his business of chasing away other birds. On every occasion, I would provide him with a breakfast of maggots (which I also used for fishing bait), and for myself, coffee and biscuits. My Little Friend provided me with good company and that all-important *"listening ear."*

I would always ask him - "How will the fishing be today?", and, "Is it going to rain?" but I never received an answer.

Sometimes, he would accompany me along the river bank, but after a short distance would always return to his "home patch", for fear he might be allowing another robin to *steal* into his territory.

My late January day started early and dark. I said goodbye to Holly Dog and a rather sleepy Auntie B, and set out to meet my old boyhood friend Tom for a day's fishing on our usual stretch of river Wylye. Just like my little robin friend, Tom now lived close to the river, and we would meet each other only now and again. But our friendship stretched back almost sixty years to a time when Tom and I lived on the same road in the village of Saltwood. Then, we used to play together, building camps and climbing trees. Now, we fished together and joked about our childhood memories.

So there we had it; two, long friendships, separated over distance and time, both reunited on the same riverbank.

As I reached my destination, the car thermometer dropped to a record low of *minus* 14C … That's really cold!

Whilst parking the car under the bough of an old oak tree, just off a country road that overlooked the beautiful river Wylye, the sun awoke and shivered out from behind a distant, easterly hill. Nearby, I could see a gathering of silver birch trees; huddled together as if finding protection from the cold. Their spindly trunks were tip-topped with what looked like sticky candy floss, the colour of a toffee-apple glaze. They shone brightly in the new day's sunshine.

I don't think I've ever been outside on such a cold day, but without even the slightest breeze I didn't feel chilled. Each time I breathed out, tiny sunlit ice crystals sparkled all around me.

After checking my gloves were on properly, and every finger was present and correct in each of the glove-fingers, I pulled a woolly hat down over my ears.

Having collected my fishing rod and tackle from the boot of the car, I slipped a backpack over my left shoulder and carefully skated across the narrow, icy road to a hedge-lined track that made its way down a gentle slope between two ploughed fields.

In the harsh frost, the ground of the rough track was hard underfoot, as if made from jagged cast iron. Further down, I opened and passed through an old gate. Its hinges groaned and complained at being woken on such a cold morning. 'Sorry,' I whispered and gently returned the gate to its slumber.

The track soon flattened to a small widening in the path, just a few steps from a picturesque bend in the river. On the left of this clearing was a log, cut from a nearby fallen crack willow tree. Standing on its end, and looking like a toy drum waiting to be banged, the log served well as a convenient seat for a weary fisherman. I always sat on this "drum" to sort out my rod and tackle-belt before joining Tom

downstream on the riverbank. To the right of the log were broken branches of another willow, and to the left was a tangled, spiky blackthorn bush.

This is the place where My Little Friend would always welcome me. But not today. No chirp; no cheep; no chat.

'Where are you then? Breakfast being served,' I called out, whilst grabbing a handful of red maggots and a little chopped fruit from my backpack.

It was then I saw him. Not in his usual position, at the top of the bush, but quietly sitting deep amongst the blackthorn's lower branches, as if hiding from the freezing morning.

'Come on my friend! It might be the coldest day ever, but I haven't come all this way with breakfast for you to hide in the bushes. We've got lots of news to catch-up on,' I said with a jolly voice.

With no chit-chat, he hopped to the edge of the bush and just into the bright sunlight. I could see he looked dishevelled. Bare patches were partially covered by a higgledy piggle of feathers pointing in unusual directions.

Pulling off a small piece of curved bark from the willow stump, I fashioned a robin-sized food bowl. Then, filling it with sleepy maggots and small pieces of apple, I placed it close to him.

'Ah well, I must be off,' I said. 'See you later'. I received no reply.

After a few steps, I stopped and looked back, but the maggots and fruit remained undisturbed.

The river was as beautiful as I remembered it from my last visit;

perfectly flat in places, but imperfectly creased and rippling, like the bottom sheet of an unmade bed, where the river shallowed over stones and flints. The river water in this "chalk stream" is almost always as clear as water poured from a kitchen tap, and today was no exception.

I stopped midway over the old iron footbridge as I crossed to the far bank. Peaking over the railing, I could see the river weed wriggling like a thousand grass snakes dancing to the rhythm of the passing water.

On one side of the bridge, I dropped two small twigs into the current flowing underneath me. I ran to the other side of the bridge to see which stick emerged first; just like Piglet and Pooh Bear did with Christopher Robin. To my surprise only one twig appeared, spinning in celebration as it crossed the winning line. So where was the other one? I leant further over the railing, almost toppling into the ice-cold water. I could now see "Twig Two", as I named it, had been waylaid by a much larger branch, which was stuck and partly submerged under the bridge. Twig Two and "Big Branch" were in a chilly embrace, like old friends or family reunited at a cold railway station after many months apart. I left them deep in conversation, catching up with each other's news.

Meanwhile, our race winner, now festooned with a triumphant garland of "streamer weed" and still celebrating victory by returning upstream on an eddy of water, was being visited by a huge, slow-moving brown trout, rising from the deep to inspect what all the fuss was about. After congratulating the twig with a touch from its nose, the trout, clearly unimpressed, drifted back down to its home and disappeared under some ranunculus river weed.

Watching the trout, I now remembered why I was here on this freezing but wonderful day - not just to see a fish, but to catch a fish, and to meet up with my other old friend, Tom.

Next to the river path, sloping fields were snuggled under a brilliant white duvet of light snow, and I could see tufts of wiry grass peeking through the otherwise perfect bedcover. Motionless in the frozen air, "sugar-coated" cobwebs decorated the open wire-work of the fence. Normally cobwebs would be sticky and almost invisible to any passing fly, but, now visible and stiff, they stood no chance of catching unwary prey for their eight-legged maker, who was crouched behind the wooden fence post.

On my right, a light, ghostly mist was rising silently from the river's glistening surface. Occasionally, the water's perfect flatness was broken by ripples made by a small fish rising to break the surface, but it soon repaired itself and calmness returned.

As I walked along the riverbank, I noticed a large ground beetle floating downstream. It struggled on the waters' surface, as if learning how to swim, before being rescued by the passing "Twig Two", now free from conversation under the bridge and on its way again. Once safely onboard, our beetle relaxed in the bright sunshine to dry off, sat back and seemed to be enjoying the river cruise. An easy, if dangerous, way to travel from its home to a winter holiday destination.

With the path narrowing, frozen boot-prints had become like tiny ice-rinks for riverside creatures to enjoy, so I played my own game of stepping from one footprint to the next. With every pace, the ice squealed but didn't break. This noise startled a blackbird, which then flew across my path and got me thinking about My Little Friend. I wondered how he was, and felt guilty about leaving him. But the little robin was in his garden, with some breakfast, and hopefully the rays of the morning sun were working their magic by warming him up in preparation for my return later in the afternoon … just in time for tea.

As I rounded a bend in the river, I saw the familiar outline of my friend Tom, crouched at the water's edge.

We fished together throughout the morning and had a great time, but I found it difficult to concentrate. Even though it was so cold, the grayling, a type of fish, were more than keen to come out and play. As ever, Tom caught most of them and teased me about what a poor fisherman I was. All the fish were safely returned to their watery homes to battle another day.

Just after midday, Tom and I enjoyed a picnic lunch of hot soup, cold pork pies and delicious cheese sandwiches, prepared by Auntie Bridget the previous evening. We laughed and joked about our long friendship before saying our farewells, and I returned along the river path to see how the robin was feeling.

My Little Friend wasn't in the blackthorn, nor was he amongst the willow branches. Then I found him, lying on his side in the long grass. His eyes were open but grey and lifeless; his head and wings hung limp; his legs were straight and stiff. I cupped my hands around his cold little body, then lifted him up and breathed a long, warm

breath over his ruffled feathers.

He didn't move.

His life and spirit had slipped away. I was filled with sadness and felt a little guilty for not being with him in the last moments before he died.

Gently, I placed his still body amongst a nest of fallen, crisp, brown leaves. Covering him with a blanket of dark green moss, I positioned a single snowdrop, its tear-shaped white flower unfolded, across his final resting place. Staying with him for a few minutes longer, I said my last goodbyes and slowly walked up the track.

This time the gate made no complaint as I opened it, almost as if it was showing respect for our loss.

I drove home thinking about the day; wrapped in brightness; cloaked in cold; draped with sadness, but also overflowing with magical memories of life and the happiness of two friendships that have stayed with me over so many years.

The Return

I hadn't been back to the river Wylye until last autumn. Driving home from friends in Wales, I passed the small turning that I knew led to the river. Without a second thought, I pulled off the main road and made my way along the lane to the old oak tree. Parking the car, Holly Dog and I walked down the track to where I used to sit on the log. Little had changed, but the "drum" and some of the old willow branches had gone. The blackthorn bush was still there and amongst its tangles perched a proud robin, with a small but recognisable splodge of white paint, not on the left side but on the right of his red waistcoat. This was the next generation of my little friend's family. I was filled with joy and felt connected to the wonderful Circle of Life being playing out in front of me.

'Chirp, chirp … Dit, Dit … I've heard a lot about you. Where have you been all these years?' she said. 'Oh, and by the way, have you got a maggot or two for me?… *That would do very nicely.*'

I hope you enjoyed the memories I have shared with you. At the end of this letter you'll find a wordsearch and facts about robins.

At some stage I'll try and send you one of Auntie B's coconut feeders to hang up. In the meantime, have a look out of your window for five minutes and then see if you can answer these fun but inquisitive questions:

• How many different types of bird did you see?
• Could you identify any of them? – Robin, blackbird, blue tits, starling, sparrow, pigeon maybe?
• In my next letter, we'll visit a ghostly lake and meet night predators … *If you dare.*

My finest Regards,
Uncle Steve

A Juvenile Robin – just a couple of weeks out of the nest

"Young robins, on the other hand, are brown and scruffy. It's as if they've just fallen out of bed, forgotten to brush their hair, or put on their red jumpers before heading off to school"

That cold day on the Wylye with Tom, the robin, me and a Grayling

All fish are returned to the river!

THE ROBIN'S STORY ACTIVITIES

Which TWO of the following things are TRUE about robins?

- When robins have become grownups they don't moult in summer
- Robins never migrate overseas
- Robins will sometimes fight each other to the death.
- Robins will feed other baby birds, such as song thrushes and were once thought to be members of the thrush family.
- Robins have only one brood, or family, a year and mate with the same partner for life.

The Robin's Story
See if you can find the hidden words from the Robin's Story

N	E	G	K	Z	V	M	W	O	L	L	I	W	I	W
X	N	N	R	O	H	T	K	C	A	L	B	D	Q	S
B	A	A	B	I	S	W	P	L	G	G	L	M	J	H
E	Z	E	T	X	V	Z	D	L	F	R	D	P	I	B
E	J	H	I	G	C	E	R	S	M	A	T	O	L	P
T	B	G	B	L	K	D	R	U	M	Y	I	U	Y	Y
L	Z	P	W	Y	L	Y	E	B	U	L	D	H	M	R
E	T	A	U	E	R	P	E	D	A	I	C	R	A	I
H	R	H	E	I	N	W	K	Z	Z	N	B	Y	I	S
C	O	G	F	Z	B	R	S	J	A	G	K	X	H	B
S	U	O	D	O	Y	N	T	O	G	G	A	M	X	L
U	T	L	C	G	I	W	T	Q	V	Z	R	I	A	L
R	J	A	D	B	R	U	G	B	G	I	H	N	C	R
A	W	U	O	T	V	G	Q	Z	L	K	P	D	D	F
D	B	R	M	L	R	J	Y	E	X	O	V	N	E	K

BEETLE	BLACKTHORN	COBWEB
DRUM	GRAYLING	MAGGOT
RIVERBANK	ROBIN	TROUT
TWIG	WILLOW	WYLYE

The answers can be found at the back of the book on page 233

A letter from one of the children in south London.

> 15.3.2020
>
> To Uncle Steve & Auntie Bridget
>
> Thank you for the story and the bird food
> May we put the cocanut up and a
> greedy squirl ate the whole thing when
> When he finished he turn it around
> So now nowone else he could eat it.
> and Then the same squirle came back
> and pushed the emty cocanut of the
> fence and left it.
> I really liked the story although it was
> a bit of sad at the end.
> Can we come and visit the forest you
> met your friend at. Wiggy also found a
> rat skull in the woods and took a
> vidio of to parakeet arguing.
>
> Jemima xxx

"Wiggy" is the family's name of endearment for Jemima's brother, William.

This delightful letter was written when, incredibly, Jemima was just 9 years old. It served as inspiration for the subsequent letters, and is the very best example of "The Importance of Letters"

SCARY WINTER NIGHTS

"Outdoors at night, we seem to have no friends".
"Night plays nasty tricks on unwanted strangers."

March Letter -
"Scary Winter Nights" (Inc. William's story)

(EXTRACT FROM THE STORY)

"RUN! It's the Gggghost," Paul stammered as he jumped up and knocked over his rod, backpack and chair."

"Fear and old nightmares flooded over me, along with the swirling, freezing water of the angry river."

To The Family

Dear Kids,

Thank you so much for your lovely letters. Now I need to say this, however much I enjoy receiving your letters you do NOT *have* to write back to me. When I was your age, I hated writing *thank you letters* (still do if I'm honest) to old aunties with hairy chins, and angry uncles who sent me Christmas or Birthday presents I didn't really want.

I was very interested to hear about your naughty squirrel who stole Auntie Bridget's coconut feeder. Typical! Absolutely typical! We have a visiting rat at the moment that does much the same. I've asked Holly Dog to have a word or two with him but she's not interested and he is too fast for her. Well, keep an eye on Mr Squirrel and see who else comes into your garden or the local park. I was also very excited to

read about the rat's skull you found, just the sort of object I would like for my specimen board. I'm sorry to hear you might not be able to go to school and see your friends for a while because of this irritating virus; but this may give you a little more time to keep an eye out for the beauties of nature all around us at this time of year, both in gardens and the local parks close to you. Bright yellow Brimstone and Red Admiral butterflies are waking up from their winter sleep. I even saw a small Tortoiseshell butterfly land on my wall to enjoy a little spring sunshine. Lots of female, Queen bumblebees, full of eggs, are looking for homes at the moment, so take a close look at the coloured rings around their bodies and see how many different bees you spot when you're out walking. You might find one with a white bottom, that's actually politely called the White-"tailed" bumble bee. Ooh! And a song thrush has just landed outside my window. It's all happening in nature at the moment.

With all this time on our hands I thought you might like another story or two ... actually **THREE**.

Now, I'm a little worried you may find them a bit too scary, but these are events that actually happened to me, and I'm still alive to tell the tales. The stories show you how I dealt with my fears, and they may also help you to know you are not alone with your thoughts when sometimes you're feeling a little frightened. Well here goes ... *if you dare*.

The stories are about two very different locations, set almost fifty years apart. But both places are linked. They are linked because each is about night-time discovery, including creatures and demons of the night. The stories peer into my fears of darkness, especially in the Great Outdoors, and the fears we may share in our dreams and nightmares. If that hasn't put you off … *read on.*

Firstly, I wonder if you have ever walked around your bedroom at night when it's been so dark you couldn't see where you were going. You may have bumped into your bedroom door or stubbed your toe on the leg of the bed. Possibly you've stumbled over a chair, or some toys in the middle of the floor. Things you're familiar with in your daily life become hurtful hazards at night. The more we stumble, bump and trip, the less we trust our surroundings. We become uncertain, wary and sometimes fearful. Even in our own bedrooms, we can become afraid of what we can't see.

"Simple," I hear you say, "I'll just turn the light on" … But what if there is no light switch, and you're not in your comfy bedroom with friendly toys and a warm duvet; rather you find yourself outside, all alone in a wild, dark and unfriendly forest. *How might you feel then?*

When I go wild walking or fishing at night, I feel I'm dropping into another world. Summer nights are short; the days are long; the air is warm; the moths are lazy, and all is calm … *In the depths of winter, it is very different.*

At night, in winter, the fields and forests, lakes and rivers, even local parks and gardens can make me feel like an unwelcome guest. A feeling that maybe I shouldn't be there; a feeling of venturing into a world and time for "others". You and I own the day, but the night is a time for creatures of darkness; some familiar and many unfamiliar.

So, together let's discover a little more about these secret, night-time worlds.

***

The outdoor winter nights

The small comfort lent to us by a weak winter sun soon disappears, along with its feeble light, in late afternoon. As dusk creeps into darkness, the night wraps around us with a powerful grip. In the fading light, our sense of sight is dimmed, but, our hearing and imagination are both ignited; like a match being dragged across a matchbox.

In winter, you can smell sweet decay in the darkness. The trickle of a summer's stream becomes a raging river, getting louder by nightfall; telling you to *"leave; leave NOW"* … "This is not your world." … "There is danger all around."

Outdoors at night, we seem to have no friends.

Bushes, visible on your daytime journey, now seem to cross your path and conspire amongst themselves to trip you up in the darkness. Paths become slippery or simply disappear as you creep through the forests or woods. Twigs on low hanging branches, absent of leaves and life, flick your face as you slowly pass. In the wind, tall, dark trees murmur or even roar their anger at your presence. Gates refuse to open as easily as they once did. And, country stiles, bedecked with brambles, are ready to snag your clothing; seeking out exposed skin with their knife-like thorns.

Night plays nasty tricks on unwanted strangers.

But, surprisingly, I LOVE this time of night; this time of year and these wild worlds on our doorsteps.

As a child, at the age you are now, I had fear-filled dreams; chased by demons I could never see. Always, I felt at the mercy of my nightmares; fearful of falling off tall trees or being chased by unseen beasts up crumbling buildings ... But now, only a little older, I know when I'm dreaming, and the shadowy creatures slip defeated into the darkness... *I'm in control!* ... And, that is the way I now feel about being outside on winters' nights; strangely powerful and in control.

But there were two nights when my confidence was tested; once when I was a little older than you are now, and again just a few years ago.

I'd like to tell you about them, so read on if you dare

Ghost Lake

I need to take you back to when I was a boy, living in a village called Saltwood, close to the seaside.

From the age of eight, I would fish in a secret pond, not far from my home, which the local children called Ghost Lake. The pond nestled deep in a little, steep-sided valley, and it was surrounded by great oak trees, tall beech trees and a few stunted weeping willows. It was very overgrown and difficult to reach. Its small brick-built paths and little holding ponds; waterfalls and weirs had been over-run by the slow creep of nature. Old rambling rhododendron bushes and blackberry-laden brambles were now in charge of this magical kingdom.

The pond, hidden and forgotten for so many years, held dark secrets. It concealed two small islands, each about 20 metres in length. One was connected to the mainland by a dropped tree. The other one had a tiny iron connecting footbridge, now fallen into decay. But with a little bravery, a well balanced small boy or girl was able to edge slowly across the single remaining rusty beam, a metre above the stagnant water.

When across the broken bridge, and with a lot of searching through the undergrowth and broken trees, this island's secret was revealed … Two ancient graves; one of a man called William, and the other his dog, named Daisy. Both graves were draped in ivy and deadly nightshade. Dark green moss partially hid their long-forgotten names, whilst weeping alder bushes bowed and knelt in sorrow over the ancient tombstones.

It was said, by an old farmer, who lived his life nearby, that on winters' nights you could hear the sound of a ghostly spirit walking with his long-dead dog along the hidden paths that spiralled down to this haunted and darkened pond.

Well, fifty years ago, on the last day of autumn, time was pushing a warm afternoon towards the chilly winter's night. And, a gentle breeze blew through the trees, like a giant's breath blowing out a single candle. The last golden leaves of the season were released from the grip of the tallest beech trees and silently flip-flacked down to the stilled water's surface below. All around was painted in twilight grey, a special colour only seen at this time of day and this time of year. The air was richly filled with that sweet scent of autumn decay.

On this very day, my school friend Paul and I had been fishing since mid-morning. And having enjoyed a packed lunch of cheese sandwiches and freshly baked Victoria sponge cake for tea, we really should have been on our way home to the comfort of an open fire and cup of hot chocolate. But we weren't.

Now, it must be understood that all young, and some not so young, fisher-folk want "just one more cast" of their fishing lines into the water, hoping it will bring the biggest fish of the day to their bait. We were now fishing much, much later than we were allowed.

In the dark gloom, a thin grey mist started to prowl towards us across the glass-like surface of the water from the islands. Soon we could hardly see each other, let alone our fishing floats, far out in the mist.

Without warning, we both heard a deep groaning sound coming from the direction of "Grave" Island … Then nothing; all was silent; not a flicker of wind; not another leaf dropped. All that lived seemed to be peering through the thickening veil towards the shadowy distant island.

I held my breath, and the only thing I could hear was my heart thumping as I remembered the farmer's folk tale. We froze as a minute seemed like an hour, or was it just a second, until far over to our left, we heard a ghostly rustling, followed by a loud "tink … tink; clank … clank," of what sounded to me like a metal leash or collar holding back a wild dog.

Suddenly there was an explosion of noise and movement, not from the direction of the rustling or clanking, but from Paul.

'RUN! It's the *G-g-g-ghost!*' he stammered as he jumped up and knocked over his rod, backpack, and chair. Then, he started to hop from foot to foot with a look of white terror on his face as he pointed into the mist enveloped bushes. For a moment, I was more frightened by Paul's appearance than the possible appearance of the ghost with his long-dead dog.

I joined Paul in his panic.

'Throw the fishing kit behind the hedge,' I shouted, whilst waving my arms in the direction of the undergrowth behind us.

With that, chairs, fishing rods, tackle boxes and bait, including maggots and a loaf of bread were thrown into and over the brambles behind us before we started running for our lives.

With the noise following close behind, we scrambled up a narrow track and over the rotting timbers of an old, dilapidated 5-bar gate. From there, we ran full-pelt down to the stream and across a planked bridge to an upward sloping sheep field, only to be met, once again, by the menacing fog that seemed to be trying to cut-off our escape.

Hardly taking a breath and without looking back, we blindly pushed on, deeper into the murk. Still running, albeit somewhat slower, I now saw the silhouette of a tall, dark figure, accompanied by a large dog, drifting through the mist and down the field towards us. Should we try to scurry back down to the stream and away from the mysterious dark figure coming nearer and nearer, or continue running from the grip of the ghost and his wild dog behind us? What if the phantom and his hound had been able to mysteriously move in front of us?

Trapped in the middle, we hadn't got the energy to run any further. Our end was near, and we gave up all hope of life. Exhausted, I dropped to my knees and covered my eyes.

***

Out of the gloom, I heard a deep voice coming from the "dark figure."

'Err, and what time do you call this?'

It was my father; sent by my concerned mother to walk our dog, Lucy, and collect us from the lake.

I had never been so pleased to see him as I was that night.

'It's the ghost, he's right behind us,' I choked out, whilst still lying on the ground, desperate to explain but also needing to get some air into my burning lungs.

'He was huge, wearing a massive black coat and hood. His dog was like a wolf, and they almost caught us,' Paul exaggerated in his overexcitement as he pointed back down the slope.

All four of us peered back towards the sinister darkness of Ghost Lake, nestled at the top end of the valley, but there was nothing to be seen, except the slowly retreating, swirling mist.

Having got our breath back, we trudged home with a great tale to tell our friends. And you'll not be surprised to hear, I never fished there again after dusk!

The next morning, my aunt walked with Paul and me back to the lake to see if our fishing equipment was still there. It was ... except all the bread had disappeared. Had the ghost of Daisy Dog with her owner visited us and eaten the loaf? We never discovered the truth of what we heard. In fact, neither Paul nor I ever agreed on exactly what we'd seen that scary night.

I'm going to leave it for you to decide.

***

Over many years afterwards, I fished in the pond, by myself and also with friends. We made camps from fallen branches and large ferns; discovered paths and disused tracks, and found steps crafted from wood and stone on the valley sides.

In springtime, we would visit Grave Island, leaving posies of late-flowering snowdrops and early-flowering primroses, bound together with strands of long grass, collected on the way to the pond. On one occasion, we left dog biscuits and planted crocus bulbs below Daisy's headstone. The visits became less frequent as we got older. But when we did go back, we always celebrated with picnics of jam sandwiches and homemade cakes. I saw wildlife as never before; with herons resting in trees and water voles scurrying across the stream.

The demons and ghost, I once ran away from were now put to an easy rest. The pond had become friendly and even homely; a secret place where children ran free to explore without grownups to interfere. A wild and wonderful world.

"Esox Lucius" – The Beast from the Deep

Now, that's not quite the end of the story because Ghost Lake had one last secret to reveal. Beneath the surface of the dark deep water was said to live a killer of huge size, a beast so feared that none would venture even into the shallows. Stories of moorhens being dragged from below the waters' surface and never to be seen again were matched by tales of ducks, even dogs being pulled to their death in the depths of this watery grave.

In truth, we never actually saw this deadly monster. But, on one lazy summer afternoon, I was fishing, and reeled in a very small roach, a species of silver-coloured fish, when it was grabbed by a slightly larger, greedy and somewhat ambitious perch, a carnivorous stripy fish with a formidable set of spines along its back. So, now I had two fish, one trying to eat the other and both on a single hook. This was unusual but not unheard of. Even to this day, I can hardly believe what happened next. As I pulled both fish towards the safety of the bank, the water behind them mysteriously darkened.

In an explosive frenzy, both Mr Roach and Mrs Perch disappeared from view and my rod bent into a tight curve. Instead of the fishing line coming towards me, as I wound it in, it was suddenly being pulled away. For a moment, I had not one, not two, but THREE creatures on my single hook.

As quickly as it had begun, the monster and Mrs Perch released Mr Roach, and my rod sprang from its curve to being straight once more. This, in turn, catapulted the line out of the water and into a hedge behind me.

There it was, all in a tangle, hanging like a makeshift Christmas decoration; the line; the coloured float; the fishing weights; the hook …. and a dangling Mr Roach! I guess not surprisingly, he looked somewhat stunned but none the worse for his adventure. After all,

Colour me in!

he'd been caught on a hook; partially eaten by a fish *and* a mysterious "monster", then flown through the air before finally coming to rest in a bush.

'Wow,' I said, 'you've got a great story to tell your friends when you get home. I bet they won't believe you.'

With that, I checked him over for injuries before making sure neither the perch nor "The Monster" was around and then slipped Mr Roach back into the pond. He sat in the shallows for a minute or two before gingerly returning to the deep to fight another day. I've no idea what happened to Mrs Perch, but hopefully, she got away from the clutches of the monster.

A question for you: So, who, or what, do you think the "Monster from the Deep" was? Well, to find out you're going to have to read the next part of this story. We'll meet him again, *fifty years later,* on a cold, windy winter's night. But first, I need to transport you, not only through five decades in time but 150 miles away, from Ghost Lake to a special river, where we'll also meet other creatures and have some scary moments.

What I will tell you is his name. His ancestors terrorised pools and rivers when dinosaurs ruled the earth … His name is *"Esox Lucius"*. The Wolf of the Water.

***

Esox Lucius - Fifty Years Later. (William's story)
As a young boy, my friends and I would stay overnight at each others' homes before going fishing together. We would frighten one another with stories of river monsters, and Esox was never far

from our imaginations. Although we had fear in our hearts, our spirits secretly wanted to catch one of these creatures … and so it came to pass.

Well, this story is not just about *Esox Lucius*. It brings *Esox* together with an oft-forgotten little river, another predator of the darkness, and a bleak winter's night.

Now, I need to tell you a little about the river and Esox Lucius.

Let's start by discovering the river. It's called the Lod, and, for a river, it's tiny and shy, sneaking its way through the Sussex countryside without fuss or fanfare. In fact, some local people hardly know it's there until it floods and blocks the odd country road, which it does when ignored in autumn or winter. At its top end, what we call the "Upper Reaches", our little river avoids all villages and towns … as I said it's very shy! In some places, and with a good run-up, you could jump over it with a single bound. The river twists and turns, often it seems just for fun; just for the sake of it. The Lod nestles in its own little valley, with small sloping fields on either side and abandoned woodlands for company along its course.

You would be forgiven for thinking only small fish, such as sticklebacks and minnows would live in this little stream, but it has one not so little secret. Just two kilometres downstream from one of my favourite pubs there is a huge old derelict millpond that is home to big fish - and I mean very big. Well, often with big fish come even bigger predators.

I'd been given permission from a farmer to fish a private stretch of the river. To get to it, I had to walk down through two rather dishevelled fields, which were often inhabited by Romney sheep in summer and belted Galloway cattle in the spring. Both sheep and cattle were given some protection on rainy days by small clusters of stunted willow trees, whose lower branches had been nibbled away by the bored young bullocks. Football sized rocks and larger boulders lay strewn across the valley sides, often nesting in clumps of long grass or below untidy bushes. In winter the cows would be given shelter from floods and storms in a cosy, straw-filled barn on the other side of the farm.

Downstream, beyond the fields and connected by a disused wooden "kissing" gate, lay an ancient dark forest. The river crept from the fields to the forest under a wire fence, now distorted, bent and broken by years of vicious winter floods. Old moss-covered chestnut fence posts, broken and bowed, had long since given up their duty of holding the wire in place. The posts, now without a job of work to do, lazily marked the boundary between the farmland and the trees.

Here, at the edge of the forest, the river really came to life. Freed from the confinement of the fields, it skipped around, danced under, and leapt over fallen trees. Sometimes it even flowed over the body of a roe deer or badger, who'd once dared to venture too close to the crumbling banks of the over-excited, swirling river. In the twilight world of the forest, where even the midday light feared to enter, the river crafted deep pools of turbulent, writhing water as it met massive immoveable roots of willow trees or rocky outcrops. In these deep dark pools lurked danger, not only for small and even large fish, but also for mice, rats, and voles that fell into, or tried to venture across the river.

You might ask why anyone would be interested in going near such dangerous pools. Well, not only can the river's current pull unsuspecting creatures under the water but this is where *Esox Lucius* often lurks to entrap his prey.

He has no respect or compassion for young or old; for mammal or fish; for duckling or stoat. Without fear, he moves silently from lakes and millponds to gently flowing rivers and onto raging torrents.

Watching, always watching, *Esox Lucius* lies on the river bed amongst the weed and stones, perfectly camouflaged; perfectly still, until he sees, or smells; or senses his prey above. Then, his huge tail accelerates him, with immense power and speed, upwards. His massive mouth can be as big as a wolf's mouth and is armed with 500 backward facing needle-like teeth. He snaps his jaws closed around his victim and drags them deep to their death. Esox has one other particularly chilling trait. Not only will he eat fish and mice, but he also preys on others of his own kind, including his own children!

Now you may have noticed I always referred to Esox as "him" or "he". I do this simply for ease of writing, because the biggest and meanest of all Esox Lucius' are, in fact, FEMALE. So please forgive me for continuing to call my creature, "Him" or "He".

Enough of this general chit chat. It's time to tell you of two days that eventually brought me, one winter's night, face to face with this

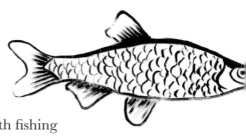

elusive predator; this creature
of my nightmares, fifty years
after my first encounter at
Ghost Lake.

Two years ago, I was fed up with fishing
at my local pond and decided to visit and fish this stretch of the
Lod. Parking my car on the side of a little country road, Holly Dog
and I walked the short distance to a metal 5-bar-gate. It opened
up to a path that slipped its way down through the rag-tag fields of
long grass and boulders to a tiny bridge spanning the river. Moving
downstream, I started to fish using my favourite small float, under
which dangled a single and rather reluctant pink maggot for bait,
whilst Holly Dog chased two surprised rabbits into the safety of a
nearby bramble thicket. Showers of rain came and went, arm in
arm with intervals of sunshine. It was a typical early winter's day.

Holly Dog and I slowly worked our way down the riverbank as
the greedy roach and dace gladly gobbled up my hapless maggots.
Many got hooked and were brought flapping to the bankside. And,
after brief and polite introductions, all the fish were returned to their
watery home without incident.

This was until we reached a left-hand bend in the river, just short
of the old wire fence where the river escaped from the fields and
disappeared into the forest. In its usual manner, my float bobbed and
waggled its way down with the flowing water, twisting and turning
as if chatting with each riverside scrubby bush it passed. My float
suddenly steadied itself at a jaunty angle, said "Well, I must be off,"
before diving out of sight under the water. As I lifted the rod, the

line tightened and my hook connected with another fish. This was different from the others I'd caught as it pulled from right to left then right again, trying to reach the safety of submerged roots. From previous experience, I knew it was a fish called a Chub, which was confirmed when eventually it reached the surface and glided towards me like a little ship under tow from a tug. It was the biggest fish I'd caught that day and measured about one and a half times bigger than my hand and three times as thick. I lowered a special net, called a landing net, into the edge of the water in preparation for the arrival of the fish, to lift it out of the water. Just before I glided Mr Chub over the net, the water erupted around the surprised fish.

As if a bomb had exploded, waves of frothing water were sent crashing to the riverbank. Huge swirls appeared; this way and that, as water splashed into my face and over both my jacket and the crouching Holly Dog. It was then, in the centre of the commotion, I saw him; The Beast; the monster; the killer; the mighty Esox Lucius. In less than a second Lucius had disappeared, taking the chub and my float deep under the surface of the river. In the same instant, my rod bent double, almost being pulled from my hand. A moment later, the line snapped; the rod straightened and my old beloved float bobbed up from the deep. Free from the line the float laid flat on the water as if dead. It drifted under the wire and into the forest, never to be seen again.

Dazed, still shocked, and with Holly Dog barking furiously, I dropped to the ground; rod in one hand, and empty net in the other. I must have looked like a zombie, but slowly I recovered and I started to realise what had happened just seconds before. With my fishing line in tatters and my heart still racing, the two of us decided this had been enough excitement for one day. I was determined to return the following evening, better prepared for the fight ahead ... Holly Dog was not so sure!

Up to this point, you may have noticed I haven't actually told you who or what Esox Lucius really is. Yes, I've said he has a powerful tail, a huge mouth and much more, but now it's time to tell you exactly what I was up against before we venture together into the forest in the hunt for Esox Lucius. I have said before Esox Lucius may mean "River Wolf", but this is no ordinary wolf, oh no. Females may live up to twenty-five years, grow to well over a metre and a half   long and weigh over twenty kilograms. It is often said that our biggest, non-sea dwelling, native, wild carnivore is the badger or red fox, but I believe it's Esox, who can be twice the weight of either. So what is he? Esox Lucius is a fish but no ordinary fish, a living fossil, which we commonly call the PIKE for short. Young ones are often called "Jacks", which is a reference to the Devil.

Now we've been properly introduced, it's time to enter the deepest parts of the forest in a night time pursuit of the monster of my childhood dreams and nightmares ... If you dare!

The following day the weather had turned cold and wet, and the wind blew steady from the chilly north-west. A misty drizzle greeted me as I arrived at the top of the valley early that evening.

Colour me in!

Holly Dog had decided this was one adventure too many and stayed at home, tucked-up in front of the open fire. A dark patchwork of cloud raced overhead, not wanting to wait and witness the possible demons that lay before me in the forest. The atmosphere was very different from the day before; unwelcoming and almost hostile. I made my way down to the river and along to the old gate, which refused to open. Squeezing through a hole between the gate and what remained of the wire fence, I struggled to find the path that no longer welcomed visitors. It was getting dark as I entered the forest … time to turn on the small torch, which was strapped to my head.

Dense thickets of hawthorn and brambles fought for space below tall oaks and sycamore trees. But soon, the forest gave way to a new, more open, wet world of sedge grass, wild ferns and mosses, some the colour of a leprechaun's hat. All sat under a stunted umbrella of alder, willow and silver birch trees. These rare and often hidden woodlands are called Carrs (not the cars mummy and daddy drive). These Carrs are home to frogs, toads, bugs, bats and beavers, but only on very rare occasions. The ground was boggy and offered an uncertain footing. This caused me to slip and slide as I stumbled over fallen tree-trunks and decaying branches. Rotten silver birch tree stumps crumbled when I leant on them for support. It was a strange and unfamiliar world.

Now almost completely dark and with the full moon hiding behind a solid curtain of angry cloud, only the thin beam of light from my head-torch kept me company.

Out of view but only a few metres to my right, the roaring river reminded me I was not welcome here. Distant woodland noises of a fox barking and, higher to my left, a pair of tawny owls introduced themselves with a "terwoo" from the male. A shrill squawked reply from his female mate sent a chill down my back.

A quietening in the sound of the river got my attention. This was just what I wanted to hear … a pool of slower moving water.

'Excuse me,' I apologised to a scrubby bush as I pushed through. Then, ducking under yet another partially snapped tree trunk, I saw in the torchlight an open patch of ground, no more than three metres in width. It sloped dangerously towards a swirling dark pool, below an overhanging willow tree, whose roots had helped create this deep water as it pushed the river well over to the right. It was just what I was looking for. As deep as I stand high, this cauldron of water was exactly where a large Pike would lie in wait for its next unsuspecting victim. But this time the roles of hunter and hunted were about to change. Esox was about to be hunted … or so I thought.

Quietly, I knelt on the ground and fixed my fishing rod together. Pulling the line from the attached reel, I ran it through the rings along the length of the rod. Then, I tied onto the line a set of hooks and a smelly mackerel fish to attract Esox Lucius. I put a large landing net to my left before gently dropping the mackerel bait at the top end of the pool on my right. I could feel it drifting deeper and deeper in the swirling water until, eventually, it came to rest on the riverbed. Turning off my head-torch to conserve the battery, I then tightened the line. The air hung heavy with anticipation in the blackness.

Seconds turned into minutes; minutes crawled into hours, and still, I sat on the damp sloping bankside. I was cold, stiff and felt very alone. As the air temperature dropped, the clouds broke to reveal the bright but chilling Wolf Moon; the first full moon of winter. Its rays of dull silvery light danced on the rippling surface of the river.

In the moonlight there was no colour. But for the first time, faint grey details of my surrounding became eerily clear. On the far side of the river, I could see the woods were flooded with water due to the overfilled old millpond downstream. The ancient trees that still remained were nothing but dead skeletons; grey, lifeless shadows of what they once were. Their spirits had disappeared, and most had fallen to their final resting place in the sticky, stagnant mud. One or two willows still survived, but a slow death would be the eventual fate for all these trees. I was glad not to be over there as I was sure there would be no escape from the clutches of the mud.

For a moment, my fear slipped away as I became enchanted by this magical, secret world. It was then, I noticed two white shimmering shapes moving backwards and forwards through the air; ghostly and quiet; there one minute, then away across and over the hedges that ran along the top field, far away to my right. At first, it was difficult to see their outline, only visible when the Wolf Moon was at its brightest. I thought I must have been dreaming as I felt tiredness drifting over me, but the aching in my legs and back reminded me I was still awake. Back they came, both passing within metres of each other, shimmering in the moonlight. It was quite simply one of the most beautiful visions I had ever seen as I realised exactly what I was looking at. With glistening silver wings and bodies, these flying predators of the night were also hunting. Not a woodland dweller or forest phantom, but a creature of an open landscape. I was watching the soundless flight of two of our most beautiful raptors – Barn Owls. This was not a pair of barn owls seeking food to feed their baby owlets; it was far too early in the season for that. No, these were two owls, whose territories crossed for the purpose of hunting or pairing-up before the breeding season. I'd heard this occasionally happens but never seen it for myself. Magical!

Leaving my rod asleep on the bank, quietly, as if not to wake it, I pulled myself onto a tuft of sedge grass and stretched out my legs. Aaaah, relief! Still, I watched the barn owls move backwards and forwards in this dreamy twilight world.

To keep myself awake, I started to compose a little poem under my breath. It seemed strange to hear my own voice as I'd been quiet and alone for so long.

"Under gifted light from the Wolf Moon's scowl
The barn owls took flight as the wind did growl.
Esox Lucius, the Wolf Fish lay, and waited for his unsuspecting pr ...."
I froze mid-sentence ...

.... A simple "click" from the fishing reel on my rod instantly held the word "*prey*" in my mouth. A tingle of electricity moved up my arms and through my body, leaving goose-bumps in its wake. Without moving, I looked at the lifeless rod ... Then again ...'*click* ... *click*,' whispered the reel; followed by silence. Afraid to move, afraid to breathe, I watched the moonlit rod tip for signs of movement.

As if my poem had summonsed the Devil, the tip jerked once to the left, then it stopped. A second jerk accompanied a further 'click, click' from the reel. Suddenly, as if a dark spirit had entered it, the rod convulsed into life! Before I could scramble over to reach it, the rod twisted and bent towards the downstream river. The rod handle leapt into the air towards me as the tip crashed into the surface of the awakened water. I grabbed it with both hands and struggled to my feet. The reel screamed at me for help as the fishing line was being stripped off it. I pulled the rod back upstream in the hope of setting the hooks in the unseen monster's mouth as the rod bent to breaking point. The line was now so tight that when it pinged off a sunken tree root, it made the sound of a violin string being slowly plucked by a ghostly musician.

It was then I heard a mighty crash as Lucius smashed through the surface of the river downstream. With my arms hurting and the rod and line close to submission, the reel went quiet. From experience, I knew *Esox* had dropped to the riverbed to regain strength. Pike are sprinters not marathon runners, so I had a few seconds to grab my breath and get organised. I switched on my head-torch and laid out the landing net. At the ready, I had a pair of gloves to protect me from getting bitten and long forceps to extract the hooks.

I was grateful for the watchful moon, casting its silver light on the riverbank. This time I was prepared, or at least I thought I was. The rod straightened and the line went slack, so I frantically wound it back onto the reel as Esox now powered his way upstream. The line cut through the surface of the river as he swam passed, deep below me. I tried to turn myself around, but his strength caught me by surprise and I lost my foothold on the slippery bank. Falling to the ground, I felt myself sliding down the damp slope, and then it was my turn to crash through the surface of the water and into the cold, deep pool.

Fear and old nightmares flooded over me, along with the swirling and freezing water of the angry river as I struggled to get a breath. Still holding the writhing rod in my right hand, I floundered to find something to grip onto with my left. It was then my headlamp fell off into the water. Helpless to catch it, I saw its dimming light disappear into the blackness of the deep pool; leaving me alone in the dark and very afraid. Only my chest waders were keeping me afloat. But, if they filled with water, I knew I would surely sink to the bottom and drown as many creatures had done so in the past.

A thousand dark thoughts raced through my head. Would I freeze? Would I drown, or would Esox Lucius return, like the unseen demons of my childhood nightmares to exact his revenge on me? I'd been taught that if I fell in a river when fishing, I should throw away my rod, then float and drift to a safe place downstream before getting out. It was good advice, but I didn't follow it. I still had the giant fish on the line, and I wasn't about to give up.

As I scrabbled to get out of the swirling water, my left foot connected with solid rock, well below the surface. At the same time, and quite by chance, my left hand clasped a large exposed root of the willow tree. For what felt like minutes, I swung backwards and forwards; the current pushing me one way and Esox pulling me the other. I felt like a door banging open and shut in a winter gale, except I was still underwater with little more than my head and shoulders above the surface.

If I could only hold on to the rod until Esox stopped wrenching the line, I would be able to throw the rod high onto the bank. But time was running out as my waders were now fast filling with ice-cold water.

'Please stop pulling,' I pleaded in the dark to my foe as I spat out a second mouthful of freezing river water.

It was then my moment came. The tugging stopped ... I quickly released some line and threw the rod onto the bank. Holding on to the submerged roots of the willow with both hands, I pulled myself around, and behind the tree. There, I was able to make my escape from the strong current by dragging myself out of the water and onto the bramble infested river bank. Breathing heavily, I lay there for a moment, quite exhausted. Relieved and dripping wet, but with no time to spare, I struggled to my feet and blundered straight through a small alder bush, hoping to be reunited with my rod.

I was so grateful to see it was exactly where I'd thrown it. Esox hadn't raced back downstream to the millpond, and if he had, he would surely have pulled my rod with him.

He hadn't taken his chance to escape, so now I needed to take my chance to catch him. I picked up the rod and braced myself against the willow. Then, slowly I wound the slack line back onto the reel. Gently the tightening line caused the rod tip to bend, but not enough to cause *Esox* to move. A little more the rod curved until I felt the weight of him. The pressure of the line had stirred the monster to lift off the riverbed. Now I could feel every slow movement of his tail as the rod swayed with the same rhythm.

This is the magical time when fishing; a special connection is made through the line between monster fish and fisherman. Each can feel the other, communicating through the darkness by touch; each waiting for the other to make a move, a game of chess being played out in the black of night. The ultimate predator; fearless, master of his world, and me; cold, wet and crouching in this hostile and forbidding place.

But I felt in control, as fearless as my foe.

In the darkness, I'd overcome my demons and nightmares, just as I had done years before.

I tightened the line a little more, and instantly he responded by moving quickly upwards. Breaking through the surface far upstream, in an act of defiance and aggression, he sent tidal waves in all directions. Like an earthquake, or should it be riverquake, I felt his power tremble through my fishing rod. Then, at the centre of the silver-lit froth, I saw him for the first time; The Wolf-Fish in the sparkling light of the Wolf Moon.

I pulled a little harder, knowing that if I could keep him facing in my direction his huge tail would not be able to smash my line, as he had the day before. Near the surface, his great strength would soon be reduced. He thrashed the water in anger as I moved him towards me.

'Slowly, slowly,' I said to myself as I extended the landing net and sunk it deep into the freezing water in readiness for his arrival. Little by little, his energy was draining away as I drew him over the waiting net.

Once in place, I quickly raised the net around him, and in that moment he realised what was happening. Trapped, he thrashed and cursed but to no avail. Waiting until he had settled down, I dropped my rod on the ground and lay on the edge of the riverbank before grabbing the top of the net with both hands and pulling it clear of the water. He thrashed some more, writhing and beating his tail in anger.

I lowered the net to the waiting fishing mat, and there he was, glistening in the moonlight. Now, both of us were still. We met face to face for the first time. At a metre long and approximately 9 kilos in weight, his body was as thick as a small tree trunk. The beautifully mottled camouflage ran from his powerful tail, past his fins and across his great body. He fixed his eyes on me with a cold and steely gaze. His massive mouth, the size of my two hands held in prayer, was slightly open, revealing just some of his many teeth. The gape of his mouth was held open by my hooks that had just been caught in the scissors of his bony jaw. There was no sign of the mackerel.

Colour me in!

'Well my friend, here we meet; face to face on this scary winter's night,' I said, as all was now calm beneath the Wolf Moon's silver gaze.

I next had to remove the hooks. I put on my left-hand glove before moving forward and gently gripped him behind his head. He made no movement. Taking a firmer grasp, I lifted his head and using the long forceps I easily removed the hooks from his bony mouth. Still he made no movement as I lowered him back onto the mat. Now freed from the hooks, I took one more look at my foe. Then, I flicked off my glove, placed my left hand on the ground next to his body for stability and turned away to safely stow the forceps with my right.

Within a split second, he twisted on the mat and I received what felt like a forceful hammer blow on the lower part of my arm and hand. The shock sent me reeling backwards as Esox Lucius squirmed back towards the edge of the riverbank and then splashed into the deep pool of flowing water.

Still shocked and numb, I started to feel a warm tingling along my lower arm. In the moonlight, I saw blood covering the back of my hand. There was no pain at this stage, just numbness as I gained my senses.

I leant over to my drinks bottle and began to pour the clean water onto the bloodied hand, but it just wouldn't stop bleeding. So, I wrapped my hand in a handkerchief and pushed it back into the glove to apply a little more pressure. Even to this day, I have the tiniest scar on the back of my middle finger.

Feeling a little dizzy, I lay on my back, and looked through the canopy of the low trees, to the stars directly above. It was only then the throbbing started in my damaged hand.

I was very cold and soaking wet, as my waders were still partially filled with water. I was slightly injured, my torch was gone, and as I turned my head and peered into the blackness of the wood, I realised that was my only way out. The dagger-like brambles and demon-possessed branches waited for my perilous journey through the unforgiving forest. But even in the blackness, I still felt powerful and in control within this mysterious, dark world.

After a few minutes, I slowly packed up my fishing kit, took apart the rod, and for the last time looked back into the chattering pool, wondering if Esox Lucius was still there before I started to fight my way through the undergrowth.

Deserted by even the Wolf Moon, I pushed, slipped and tripped my way into the blackness of the woods without the guiding light of my lost head-torch. I was blind, often just managing to feel my way over fallen branches and around grasping brambles.

Each step was harder than the last as I became more and more exhausted with the effort of fighting the mud and foliage of the forest, in almost complete darkness. I was becoming disorientated, and my fishing equipment got entangled with every bush I encountered.

After what seemed like an age, I peered through the trees and was so relieved to see the moonlit open field, just beyond the broken fence. I pushed on, only to cut my face on a branch, and damage my waders on a menacing piece of barbed wire ... *But I was free.*

Shattered, I slumped to the firm ground of the field to regain my strength, and I took the opportunity to check I still had all my equipment. I rested for a couple of minutes before once more getting to my feet.

As I made my way up the path to the road, wet and cold, I turned to gaze over the valley, and in the distance, I saw one of the Barn Owls still hunting along the hedgerows at the top of the field, in the light of the Wolf Moon.

At that point, I wondered who had won the battle; maybe neither of us; or maybe both of us. I'd conquered my fears and demons, and Esox Lucius had exacted his revenge on me.

***

Six months later, on a beautiful day in early May, I was to play cricket at the lovely Lodsworth village green, which is very near to the large millpond, just downstream from where I had my night time adventure. It was Sunday morning and the air hung gentle and warm as I arrived at the cricket pitch. I had plenty of time to enjoy the lazy flight of dithering bumblebees and the cry of skylarks in the cloudless heavens above.

On the far side of the green, I saw the track that leads to the old millpond, and I set off with my picnic lunch to take a look at the water.

The narrow track meandered between fields of winter wheat and the overgrown hawthorn hedges that were laden with green leaves and white blossom. On reaching the pond, I was welcomed by the clattering sound of water cascading over the broken stonework of the old mill weir. I looked over the water to the far end where the river Lod entered the pond in the west. Beyond, the forest still held vivid memories of my battles with *Esox* and my night demons. How different it was now as I settled down on the bankside grass to eat my lunch.

I imagined *Esox*, still, Emperor of his domain, lurking in the depths below; waiting and watching for his next unfortunate victim. Our two very different worlds were separated by the thin skin of the water's surface: His; cold, dark and weightless; mine, warm, light and dizzy with the scents of late spring.

Quite by chance, my attention was drawn to something red and brown nestled in the reeds to my right. Intrigued, I slipped off my shoes and socks, rolled up my trousers and made my way through the shallows towards the object. Parting the reeds with my hands, I was overwhelmed with the feeling of joy of being reunited with an "old friend". For there, bobbing gently from side to side was my old fishing float, lost when the Chub was taken by Esox Lucius; and next to it a very rusty head-torch, covered in weed and silt. Both returned to me as mementoes of a wild winter's night.

***

I hope you enjoyed these stories and they weren't too scary. In the next letter, we'll meet some special garden visitors. But until then, look at the next page for a story related crossword and a very interesting Fact or Fiction quiz about barn owls.

Fine Regards
Uncle Steve

For an update and photo of Esox Lucius in the river Lod go to page 213

The river Lod in winter flood

A distant Barn Owl in flight

Mysterious Ghost Lake on a cold, mid–winter's day, half a century later

SCARY NIGHTS ACTIVITIES

Which ONE of the Barn Owl "facts" below is TRUE

- Ideally, a pair of barn owls, including successfully feeding their family, will catch up to 2000 prey animals a year.
- Barn owls digest all the bones (and fur) of their prey.
- Barn owls don't poo, they just "squirt out" a white, runny liquid.
- Barn owls have fantastic night vision and hunt mainly by sight.
- Due to their small beaks and mouths barn owls have to tear apart their dinner before swallowing it

Scary Winter Nights
Using the stories to help you, complete the crossword puzzle below

Created using the Crossword Maker on TheTeachersCorner.net

Across
2. What were the two 'flying' predators called?
4. What fell into the dark pool of water?
5. Where did I fish as a boy?
6. What is the name of the little river where Esox lived?
7. Who was The Beast from The Deep?

Down
1. What shone in the sky at night?
3. What did we throw behind the hedge at Ghost Lake?
5. What sound came from 'Grave' Island?

The answers can be found at the back of the book on page 234

GARDEN GUESTS

"You've brought WHAT home?' she said angrily.
'This is the last straw young man.'"

April Letter – Garden Guests

(EXTRACT FROM THE STORY)

"'It looks like a Dragon's tail,' I said as Adrian peered into the sky for any passing dragon that may have lost one."

To The Family

Dear Kids

I hope you are well and maybe you've been getting outside for walks in your local parks as the weather has been bright and sunny.

You may remember in the story about *Esox Lucius* I mentioned seeing a pair of barn owls. Well, we don't have barn owls visiting our garden, but we do have another type, or species, of owl called the tawny owl, and several of them hoot and toot at night throughout most of the year.

Of course, owls are not the only "bird predators" and many others will enter our gardens and parks from time to time. Often we see Buzzards and Red Kites, wheeling and diving, high in the sky above us and over the town centre. I want to put a big chunk of meat in the back garden to see if they'll land on our lawn for a spot of lunch, but Auntie Bridget's not too keen, so we'll have to see about that idea. Holly Dog thinks it's a great plan!

Sometimes we are visited by a kestrel, hovering as it looks for its next dinner of mouse or vole. And on two occasions this year Auntie B and I have seen a pair of "Hobbies" circling above the town centre trying to catch young swifts before they all fly off to Africa for the winter. A hobby is not just the thing we do in our spare time but is also the name of our second smallest bird of prey. All of these types of "avian hunter" have a family name of Raptor, like the dinosaurs. Raptor simply means a bird that catches its prey using its feet or talons.

Now, I say all of this because we've had a murder in the garden, and more on this later in the letter. But I will tell you it was a "bird murder" and I think I know who did it. All of this drama got me thinking about adventures close to home.

So, today I'm sitting at my desk, looking out of the study window on to our garden. Holly Dog is sitting next to me on "her" little sofa, under a tall lamp that's standing aglow in the corner. She's wondering when I'm going to take her out for a walk. But at the moment we have heavy clouds hanging over us like a dirty duvet, and the trees are gently applauding an uneasy breeze as tiny water droplets are peppering the glass of my window. Will it ever stop raining today?

I love writing letters to you, but a time comes when I'd prefer to be outside, looking under stones or peering into bushes for old, forgotten and abandoned nests, which once held a past generation of my garden family.

It's raining harder now. Surely there'll be nothing to see out of the window on a dreary and mucky old day like this? But then, I remind myself of what I say to the children and grownups I take fishing … "Keep looking and you will discover. Discover and you will keep looking."

I decide to take my own advice with immediate success: four tubby

and brightly dressed Bullfinches
are out for Sunday lunch, under the
overhang of a Leylandii tree. A single
Dunnock (often called a Hedge Sparrow,
even though it's not a
sparrow!) is joined by our
ever-present Robin, and

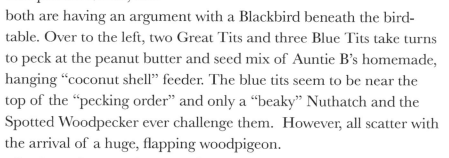

Colour me in!

both are having an argument with a Blackbird beneath the bird-
table. Over to the left, two Great Tits and three Blue Tits take turns
to peck at the peanut butter and seed mix of Auntie B's homemade,
hanging "coconut shell" feeder. The blue tits seem to be near the
top of the "pecking order" and only a "beaky" Nuthatch and the
Spotted Woodpecker ever challenge them. However, all scatter with
the arrival of a huge, flapping woodpigeon.

I enjoy going on adventures in our lovely countryside because
there is so much to see and do, and so much to discover, but as the
hustle and bustle around our bird table shows, you don't always need
to go far from home to have the best of adventures. Our gardens
and public parks can give us magical experiences.

I sense you may not believe me, so let me give you just two
examples of what happened to me yesterday and today. Early this
very morning, one of our robins flew in through our open bedroom
window and asked:

'Why is it taking you so long to get up out of bed this morning?'
He then decided to fly around the room for some exercise, just like
Joe Wicks, before leaving via the same route.' The cheek of it!

Secondly, just yesterday, I found a rat sleeping in one of our

Colour me in!

garden cage nut feeders. So I went out and gave it a poke with my finger.

'You can't sleep there,' I said. 'The birds are waiting for breakfast'. With that, he woke up, and *without* even saying "Oh, thanks for the peanuts," or "Goodbye; see you later," leapt into the hedge … *Some animals can be very rude*!

So, I thought I would share just a few of the adventures I have had in my gardens, now and as a boy growing up in the village of Saltwood. I will take this opportunity to introduce you to some of my garden guests and residents. You, and they are always welcome.

The Welcome

Twenty years ago, Auntie Bridget and I were so lucky to move into our house, just a few hundred metres from the Haslemere town centre. We have quite a big garden. In fact, it's two gardens uneasily squashed together, near the top of an awkwardly sloping hill. When the westerly wind blows, the trees get together and dance excitedly as if at a school prom or disco. Occasionally, lightning and thunder provides a spectacular sound and lightshow for these "arboreal*" parties. (* arboreal means "of trees")

We met our first garden guest on the day after we bought our new home. The house had been empty for a little while and as we walked between the low laurel hedges into the front garden we were greeted by a very, surprised and startled, miniature deer. He had tiny, partially fur-covered antlers, two rather short front legs, compared to the ones at the back, and fangs … yes, two little, backward-facing fangs, one either side of his mouth. He had a pointed face and black nose as if it had just been dipped in chimney soot. He looked as if he'd stepped out from a fairytale story. Was he a mystical woodland spirit, sent to deliver us to a hidden castle in our new magical wonderland?

Well, with delicate steps, our little "garden guide" slowly led Auntie Bridget and me around the side of the house and introduced us to our new world. Then, with a purposeful nod of his head, as if to say "My work is done," he turned away and disappeared into the undergrowth, never to be seen again.

'I can't believe what we've just seen. Or, were we dreaming?' I said to Auntie Bridget.

It was a deer, charmingly called a Muntjac. I'd only ever seen one or two of them before that day, and it would be many years until I saw another.

'I wonder what else we might discover.' I said.

The garden was wild and in most places quite overgrown. Tall pine trees competed for space with larch and oak trees. Many had fallen over because their shallow roots no longer supported them in winter storms.

Often, when a large beech tree had toppled to the ground it would knock over smaller, red berry rowan trees, like skittles in a bowling alley. Bushes, trees and shrubs provided homes for many animals. High in the tallest pines lived crows and magpies, whilst woodpeckers and nuthatches nested in holes in the dead silver birch tree-trunks that dotted the garden. Smaller birds had homes in old rhododendron and holly bushes, planted fifty years earlier. Bugs, beetles, moths and butterflies found places of safety amongst the ferns, ivy and lichens. All in all, an uneasy balance was kept; until an uninvited visitor arrived.

An Unwelcome Guest

We didn't move into the house or do any gardening for almost two years, and in that time we were visited by many animals, some seen and many unseen.

On one occasion, early in the morning, I heard a noisy commotion coming from the centre of our small woods. This was quite usual, as the garden birds, normally lead by panicking blackbirds or clacking magpies, would argue amongst themselves about who was going to sit in which tree. And, quite regularly other birds wanted to have their say over who owned which piece of the garden. Normally, these arguments would last no longer than fifteen or twenty seconds, resulting in one of the "squawkers" flying off.

No, this was very different as this commotion went on, and on, and on. The situation needed further investigation from the Garden Detective ... ME!

I crept through the undergrowth as quietly as possible, which I must say wasn't at all quiet because my footsteps crunched on last year's fallen leaves and twigs that littered the ground. Luckily, all of the birds were so involved in whatever they were getting excited about that none seemed to notice my arrival.

This was quite a gathering of well-dressed garden residents: beautifully coloured Jays with their pink and blue feathers; Magpies, smartly decked out in black and white and displaying their greenish long tails; and finally, my resident Crows, head to toe in "Undertaker" black.

All as one, the birds suddenly saw me, but instead of flying away they held their position as if asking me to sort out their disagreement.

'Well, what's up my friends?' I whispered under my breath.

For the first time I was aware they weren't arguing amongst themselves, as was normal, but with something else, or, was it *someone* else, who was the target of their excited discussions.

Without moving my clumsy, crunching feet, I bent down to peer under the nearest large laurel bush … *Nothing.* Then, I looked over to a nearby hawthorn hedge for any disturbance … *Again nothing.* By this time I had become really quite perplexed, yes that's the word, perplexed – unable to understand – what the fuss was about?

I just had a feeling something wasn't right as the birds were still anxiously cackling away, and *I was definitely missing an important piece of their argument.*

It was after I'd been standing there for at least two or three minutes that I felt the presence of another creature. Slowly, I raised my eyes, and straight in front of me I saw a large and magnificently camouflaged Tawny Owl, asleep on a branch. It was less than a metre away and a little above my head. I could have easily stretched out my arm and touched its mottled, downy chest feathers with my fingertips, but of course, I didn't.

I'm convinced that if the other birds had just shut-up for a second or two, I would have heard the owl snoring, just like Auntie Bridget after a good Sunday lunch. To this day I can't believe how our visitor slept through all that bird chatter, but it did. Turning away, I crept back to the house. The noise continued until, one by one, each of our garden birds gave up their complaining chatter and went about their normal business, leaving Mr, or Mrs Owl to sleep in peace.

At night I often hear the tawny owls in the woods at the top of the garden, but rarely see them. I've never been so close to a wild owl before and probably never will again.

Oh Deer!

Soon after the owl encounter, a workman helping me with some house renovations said he saw a roe deer give birth to a baby, which are called fawns or kids. It's a little unusual for roe deer to have just one baby, so, from a distance and using a pair of binoculars, or field glasses as they are sometimes called, I scoured the woods to find them. I could see the mother, called a doe, but no sign of any fawns. I knew at least one fawn was still in the garden because of the way the doe was acting. Her head was very upright as she turned and stomped away, taking only two or three paces before turning again to look straight at me. She banged her foot on the ground in an attempt to distract me from where her young family was hiding. I've seen this behaviour before in a nearby forest and on one occasion spotted a pair of light beige, long ears poking up from a clump of grass.

Knowing mother Roe deer will rarely stand next to her young babies, I scanned the undergrowth again with my binoculars. And

then I saw what I was looking for. Not one pair but two pairs of ears, side by side, just in front of a holly bush. I tried to get into a better position to see a little more of the fawns than just the four, long ears. But as I moved their mother made an abrupt, single barking sound, which is actually a kind of sneeze, and the ears disappeared in a flash. I didn't see them again and we left the little family in peace. A day later I wandered up to the holly bush but they were nowhere to be found, just a patch of flattened grass where the fawns had slept. Mother deer will often move their young from place to place to keep them safe and I'm sure that's exactly what had happened.

A Couple More Guests Drop By

Now and then I've seen a single hedgehog scurrying through our garden as if in a great hurry for an important meeting. If you listen carefully as they pass, you can often hear them chatting and grunting away, constantly reminding themselves of little jobs or tasks they need to complete.

'Can't stand about; things to do; worms to eat; hedgehogs to see. Must be on my way,' they mutter as they crash through the undergrowth, dragging their spiny overcoat as they go.

And last autumn I'm pretty sure we had a visit from a badger, but I didn't see it. This stripy bearlike character made a

real mess of my compost heap in an attempt to
raid a wild bees' nest to steal the honey and
eat the baby "bee-grubs". I'm not sure how
successful it was because after a couple of
days the bees were still buzzing around,
coming and going, all doing their daily
duties of collecting food for the nest of
grubs as if nothing had happened. A week

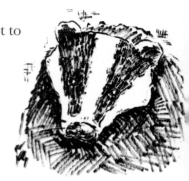

ago I saw a "queen" bumblebee looking for a new home in the same
place, so I'm setting up a camera, whilst Holly Dog stands guard. to
see if Mr Stripy returns.

***

Childhood Friends Come in All Shapes and Sizes
We have had many visits from foxes and roe deer, more on them
in my next letter, but now I want to tell you about some garden
residents that are very special to me.

Firstly, I need to take you back to a time when I was a boy, living
in Saltwood. I had an animal encounter, which is a kind of meeting,
that left me with a deep love for a very special creature … can you
guess what it was? Hmmm, probably not.

Just a few hundred metres downstream from Ghost Lake, there
was, and still is, a shallow sloping meadow. Strangely, there was a
rundown and deserted, brick-built tiny house, the colour of an old
clay flowerpot, with three rooms downstairs and two upstairs. It had
no roof; no glass in the windows, no front door and no driveway …
Just the bones of a house, standing in the middle of the grassy field. A low,

tumbled-down brick wall outlined a small front garden, and both garden and house were overgrown with brambles, clumps of grass and stinging nettles, which made it difficult to enter the ramshackle building. I'm sure my friends and I weren't allowed to play inside. But of course, we did.

Having fought our way through the undergrowth, getting stung for our troubles, we often found signs of animals that now used the building as home, including sheep, rabbits and rats. The inside of the house had a distinctive smell of rotten wood and damp paper. In each small room, bricks, rubble and glass were strewn across the old, tiled floors.

Sometimes we pretended it was our house; a house where only children were allowed. From our garden sheds, we took old chairs and boxes to use as tables; making the place a little more homely. One time we braved the rotten stairs, or what was left of them, and went to the first floor. There, we could see the house was completely open to the sky as most of the roof had long since collapsed. The few remaining floorboards and decaying floor joists were the only support for the ceiling below. Old rusty nails that once held timber planks in place, now stuck out of the wood like porcupine quills. But, the southerly views from the first-floor windows, across the valley, were beautiful. Once we lit a fire in the open grate downstairs but luckily it soon went out. Children's dreams and stories were made and told in this little shell of a house, standing quite alone in that remote meadow.

Near the stream, at the bottom of the valley, stood a dilapidated, small barn, next to a tiny stone-built bridge. Outside, it had holding pens, now long disused, for stabling farm animals. Whilst inside, old, damp and smelly straw-bales, stored over many forgotten years, were angled in collapsed piles like a giant Jenga game. This was no longer home to sheep and cattle but rather a sanctuary for voles, mice and barn owls.

On the far side of the valley lay a steep-sloping field with rabbit warrens and very tall unloved Elm Trees, often dishevelled and collapsed. I'm saddened to say, nowadays we have few old elms due to a nasty disease, but in my childhood these tall trees were home to rooks, a bird that looks very much like a crow, which nest in big groups amongst the elms' branches called "Rookeries".

I tell you this because one sunny day in late May, when I was about eleven, I was playing with two friends, Zoe and her younger brother, Adrian. We were rearranging a camp, in a downstairs room of the old house, when I heard a lot of noise coming from the  elm tree field. I could see a perfect ring of rooks standing on the grass, in the shadow of the trees. We were used to seeing the rooks spread out or arguing amongst themselves in the field, but I'd never seen them standing in a circle as if singing around a campfire.

Intrigued and excited, we ran down to the bridge near the barn, then, over the stream and up in the direction of the rooks. Halfway there and quite out of breath, we stopped. Slightly bent over and with our hands resting heavily on our knees, in an attempt to get our breath back, we were surprised none of the rooks had moved, despite our approach. Regaining some strength, we walked towards the ring of birds as they finally decided to scatter into the air in all directions.

As we got a little nearer, I saw a twisted stick at the centre of what had been the "rook circle". Zoe and Adrian stood still as I stepped a little closer. It wasn't a branch from one of the elm trees. It was greener and smoother, but scalier than any twig I'd ever seen.

'What is it?' Zoe asked from behind me.

'It looks like a Dragon's tail,' I said as Adrian peered into the sky for any passing dragon that may have lost one.

'No, wait, I think it moved; it can't be a dragon's tail,' I added.

'Why? Dragons' tails move, don't they?' said Adrian.

'Not if it isn't attached to a Dragon,' Zoe replied, knowledgeably.

It was then I realised exactly what we were looking at.

'It's not a dragon or any part of it. It's some sort of a... *SNAKE*,' I said, turning to the others.

'A snake?' Adrian questioned as he picked up a very long and bendy elm twig.

'It's a python,' Zoe screamed from a distance. 'They're poisonous, can run fast and bite!' She was wrong on all counts.

Adrian, on the other hand, was far more interested in prodding it with the twig he'd just collected.

Now, I'd never seen a snake before, except in books or at the zoo, but I was pretty sure this wasn't a python. With a little more gentle poking "our" snake started to show more signs of life as it recoiled from Adrian's attentions.

'It's alive!' I exclaimed. Wow, this *really* was exciting.

'We can keep it as a *pet*,' I went on.

Seeing the snake had moved only slowly, we gathered our collective courage and went a little closer. It was one of the most beautiful creatures I'd ever seen. We had slowworms in the garden compost and kept one or two as "pets" for a day or so, but I'd never come across anything like this.

It was difficult to work out how long the snake was, because of its twists and turns, but looking back I think it must have been just under a metre. It had yellow and black collar markings, with more splodges of black down its greenish coloured body. *Magnificent!*

The snake's lovely smooth skin had signs of damage and injury; we guessed from the nasty pecking of the rooks. I was quite sure we'd rescued the snake just in time.

'How can we get it to safety? We need to take it home,' I said.

'We could put it into one of the boxes we've got in the house,' Adrian helpfully added.

'It won't breathe in a box … Stupid,' Zoe replied to her brother. She was older and brighter than both of us but she wasn't always right.

'I know; we need a cage, and I've got just the thing back home in our shed,' I added excitedly. 'Look after the snake and I'll be back in a flash'.

'How are we going to look after it?' Zoe asked. 'It'll bite us and we'll die'.

I didn't reply as I ran down to the bridge, passed the barn and up to the top of the "house field". Ten minutes later, I was home, rummaging through the old shed in our back garden.

There it was! Rusty and dented, but a cage none the less. Not a snake cage, I grant you, but a bird cage. In fact, it'd been home to a pair of Budgerigars. It had a curved, cream-coloured wire top and sides with thick wire handles at either end for carrying it. The wirework attached to a faded yellow tray that still showed signs of hardened pooh, left by the previous feathered occupants; Chippy and Chirpy.

'Perfect,' I thought. 'Now I need something to pick up the snake with.' My dad's old thick gardening gloves were loaded into my backpack along with sandwiches and cakes for the team of Rescue Rangers, who were hopefully looking after the snake.

Somewhat more slowly, I made my way back to Zoe and Adrian with the cage. I was pleased to see all three were still in the field but a few metres away from where I'd left them. The snake had moved, and they with it.

What Now?

Having placed broken twigs and long grass in the cage, I put on the massively oversized gloves and advanced slowly towards the snake. As I approached, its tongue tasted the air.

I looked at the snake; and the snake looked at me.

'Which end do I grab?' I asked the others.

'The end furthest away from its teeth,' Zoe helpfully replied, 'or it'll kill you!' This advice didn't fill me with confidence.

The closer I got the more uncertain I became that this was a good idea. Then, to my surprise, the snake wound itself into a twisted shape, sort of rolled over onto its back; opened its mouth and gave off a foul smell.

'It's died of shock.' I yelped as I turned to the others.

My heart sank with sorrow, I'd killed it; killed this beautiful snake.

I knelt down, reached out and picked it up in the middle as its head and tail flopped down on either side of my outstretched hand. I placed the snake's lifeless body through the small cage door and onto the bed of sticks and grass. There it lay; mouth open; just a pile of dead snake.

With Adrian at one end and me at the other, we carried the coffin-cage home like a pair of undertakers; Zoe kept her distance.

I'd once kept an un-well jackdaw in the cage for a week before it recovered and was released. I even had a baby pipistrelle bat, hanging upside down by its clawed feet on a grass sieve, but I'd never kept a real snake, and certainly not a dead one.

Once home, we placed the "coffin" on the back lawn and I went inside to give the sad news to my mother.

'You've brought WHAT home?' she said angrily. 'This is the last straw young man. Mice; Bats; Birds and Bugs are one thing .... But a snake is a step ... No, many steps TOO FAR!'

'But it's dead!' I sadly exclaimed. 'I killed it,' I was almost in tears.

'Alive or Dead, I will not have it in this house.'

'It's not in the house, it's in the garden'.

'STEPHEN' ... that was never a good sign ... 'STEPHEN, GET IT OUT OF THIS GARDEN – RIGHT NOW!'

I was just beginning to realise that not everybody shared my new love for snakes – Unbelievable! Quite unbelievable! It was dead, I killed it, and I was expecting sympathy. Clearly, I'd made a huge misjudgement.

I was promptly grabbed by the arm and marched outside to

dispose of the body. My mum stood well back as she pushed me towards the coffin-cage.

With a heavy heart, I peered into the cage through the wire ... And, to my amazement, there it was ...GONE!

I then saw the snake wriggling through the garden grass to my left and on towards the compost heap.

'He's ALIVE!' I shouted as I turned towards my mother. 'He's ALIVE!'

A feeling of great relief and excitement flooded over me. I hadn't killed it after all. In fact, it had squeezed through the wire of the cage to freedom.

Clearly, this was not an emotion I was sharing with my mum as she screamed, turned, picked up the hem of her skirt and ran back to the safety of the house. It was the first and last time I'd ever seen her run anywhere.

"Strange," I thought!

I never saw the snake again, despite always looking in the compost heap over many years.

So, I have a question for you, before I continue.

Now, you will have noted I haven't told you which type or species of snake we encountered when I was a child.

What do you think it was? Zoe thought, a Python, or Cobra maybe? – No. We have three species of snake in Great Britain – Adder, Smooth Snake and Grass Snake – but only one of these behaves or "acts" like the snake in my story, so which was it?

Well, it was a beautiful grass snake.

Gloria and Friends

Now, that was a story about my "childhood" snake encounter, which brings me neatly to my "*grownup*" garden snake experiences, here in Haslemere. From that day, back in Saltwood, to the time Bridget and I moved into our house, I'd never seen snakes in any garden. Or maybe I just hadn't looked closely enough.

Over the years I've cleared the garden of some of its trees and bushes. I have a little regret in doing this because it disturbs the natural balance. But one creature's partial loss of habitat can provide opportunities for others to flourish. I've left the top of the garden wild and rugged and this connects nicely with land owned by our neighbours. I pile up fallen small branches from our trees and gather together old leaf litter and grass cuttings to give homes for mice and voles, which in turn provides great hunting for tawny owls and foxes. I also make sure I keep log stacks, cut from fallen trees and bigger branches, dotted around the garden.

It was one such wigwam of a log-pile that proved to be the most interesting. Three years ago, in late spring, this became home to a huge female grass snake. Well, Gloria, as she was known, was not only beautiful to me but she also had many admirers in her Grass Snake Kingdom. As soon as she took up residence in her woody palace, lots of male snakes came a running, or should I say crawling. At one point I counted over five snakes in her castle. I may have made a few counting errors as it became difficult to be certain which tail belonged to which head. A complication made worse because every time I went close to the woodpile most of the snakes that were visible, as they basked in the spring sunshine, disappeared into the castle fortification and out of sight.

At one point I covered the Palace with a waterproof sheet to keep them warm and dry whilst we had a spell of wet weather. This caused yet more snakes to arrive and take advantage of this desirable residence.

Often grass snakes are happy to live with adders but in all the years we've been here I've only seen a single adder, which I think is a shame as I'd like to see more, but I'll keep looking.

Gloria was quite a character, popping up in all sorts of places; wriggling across the back lawn one day, only to be discovered cooling off in the depths of our very little pond by Auntie Bridget on another. Both were equally surprised to meet each other without a prior invitation.

On one memorable occasion, the family for whom these letters were originally written visited us. And when the children were playing in the back garden, their daddy went to get something from his car, which was parked at the front of the house. As he opened the door who should he meet … Gloria, sunning herself near the porch.

'Do you know what I've just seen?' he said, on returning from the car, 'A large snake in your front garden.'

'Aah!' I exclaimed, 'That's just Gloria the Grass Snake, she lives here with us. Or, us with her, I'm not quite sure'.

Gloria also liked to travel, often to be found in neighbours' gardens. Once I received a call from a friend who lives across the road. Dill (yes that really is her name) found herself unable to leave her house via the front door because a snake had been "waiting for hours on the front step with its head down a drain."

'I'll be straight over,' I said.

So, armed simply with a single glove, I walked across to see what all the fuss was about, only to find Gloria had grabbed a very large resident toad, head-first, in an effort to have an easy lunch. Mr Toad had puffed himself out and was far too big to eat, even for Gloria. So after telling her off for being greedy and "biting off more than she could chew," I separated both parties, leaving Mr Toad to stumble back into the drain as naughty Gloria was hauled home to the Palace by me, and Dill was finally able to leave her house.

'Don't do that again, you'll get both of us into trouble,' I muttered to her.

I haven't seen Gloria for a few years now, but every summer her children popup from time to time. Last year, a small male loitered on our patio before climbing up the wall, then, he scurried across the lawn and disappeared into a bush. Auntie B and Holly Dog are frightened of all snakes, so both hid inside until his departures had been confirmed.

Another young female decided to have a look around my little shed, in the woods. I guess, with the aim of setting up a new home. I pointed out that she wouldn't be able to reach the catch on the door, to open it, and redirected her to the compost heap.

Gloria may live for over fifteen years, and in summer lay up to 35 eggs, which should hatch in the autumn. So, I'm hopeful she may be back to see us soon.

More than once, I've stopped my car to rescue a grass snake or two from a roadside gutter; put them into a Tesco's bag and handed the bag and contents to Auntie Bridget. She's absolutely petrified of worms let alone snakes. After a few screams from Auntie B, and a lot of wriggling about from the snakes, we release them in a safe space nearby.

Snakes are vulnerable on roads, where they often get run over. And summer brings more peril as the hot tarmac burns their delicate skin.

Grass snakes do NOT bite people, they may hiss a little and pretend to strike, but their main defence is to act as if dead and rotting, just like the snake did when I was a boy. Not much of a defence. They need looking after. If you find an adder, just leave it alone and it will soon scamper off.

***

The murder

News Flash -Whilst Auntie Bridget was reading the above letter, we had a flying visit from a "female" Bird of Prey, sometimes called Raptors. Following her arrival, I have to report a second MURDER!

I can reveal the first victim was a woodpigeon and now a blackbird has fallen prey to the killer … Our "murderess" left only the feathers, which I've collected for our specimen tray. Females of this species tend to eat bigger birds than the smaller males do. Who do you think committed these garden "crimes"?

Now, the murderess I spotted was … A Sparrowhawk

When hunting, sparrowhawks fly low and very fast, and if you happen to be in the garden at the time of an attack it can give you quite a shock. They are one of the most beautiful garden and woodland birds but they do like eating our resident feathered friends.

***

Well, I think it may finally have stopped raining, Holly Dog is getting restless for her walk, and time is getting late. My garden family is preparing to settle down for the evening, so time to head out and breathe in that lovely fresh, damp, sweet-smelling air. I wonder what I might discover.

I hope you have enjoyed these stories about the exciting adventures to be found in our back gardens and parks.

Your garden or local park may not be the same as ours, but it can be just as interesting. If you find a corner, where it's a little overgrown, go and look to see what's there. Now, clear a small area, say 30cm by 30cm, to expose the soil. Cover the soil with a slab or stone of about the same size. Make sure there are some little gaps between the edges of the slab and the ground, but with the slab resting mainly on the soil. Leave well alone for a week, and then have a look underneath. You might find millipedes (some black, some red), woodlice (can they roll up?), beetles even a slowworm. Slowworms are not snakes, but lizards without legs! Have a look every week, and keep a note of how life changes under your stone. A naturalist friend of mine has just sent me a photo of two slowworms he found under just such a slab only yesterday … *Amazing, don't you think?*

Have some more fun and enjoy the *Garden Guests* activity page.

In my next letter, I will introduce you to a special friend.

My very best regards,
Uncle Steve

A female Great Spotted Woodpecker

"Gloria" being returned
home after biting "Mr Toad"

A very rare visitor – A Nightingale!

GARDEN GUESTS ACTIVITIES

Garden guests – Fact File. Which ONE of these statements is FALSE?

• Grass snakes are Britain's largest reptile and lay eggs. However, adders give birth to LIVE young.
• Unlike the native deer of Britain, Muntjac Deer breed (rut) all year.
• Unfortunately, hedgehogs can't swim and often drown if they stumble into garden ponds.
• Female sparrowhawks are up to twice the weight of males.
• Brown rats can grow to half a metre in length from nose to tail tip and are more often "right-handed".
• Tawny Owls are quite capable of wading in ponds and catching fish
• A Great Spotted Woodpecker can peck up to 20 times a second.

The answers can be found at the back of the book on page 236

Can you help Gloria find her way through the crazy maze below?

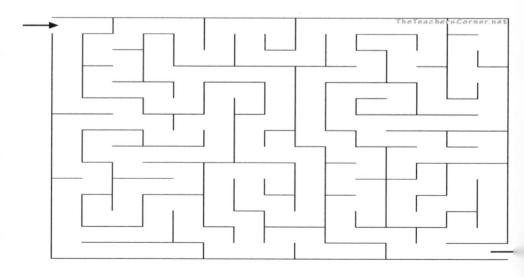

Garden Guests Word Search

See if you can find the words from the puzzle

```
Y  W  O  O  D  P  E  C  K  E  R  B  C  K  T
Y  X  V  V  S  H  V  S  T  G  E  R  O  Y  A
E  I  M  C  J  V  U  A  S  I  C  Q  K  J  W
A  J  S  E  H  C  N  I  F  L  L  U  B  I  N
R  D  K  S  L  A  Q  J  X  A  B  A  T  T  Y
L  P  D  L  F  R  K  E  X  U  W  G  V  M  O
N  U  T  H  A  T  C  H  D  U  C  P  T  U  W
E  R  H  B  O  F  F  G  R  P  S  I  T  N  L
J  Z  B  T  A  B  E  F  P  O  L  R  V  T  T
L  I  Z  L  Z  R  B  D  G  O  O  Q  O  J  Q
T  X  L  B  I  B  E  Y  F  G  W  H  G  A  B
E  Q  L  G  P  H  W  L  G  V  W  O  Q  C  C
D  H  A  A  I  R  O  L  G  R  O  T  M  Y  V
A  R  R  X  W  J  F  H  O  I  R  L  Q  H  E
U  Y  B  A  T  S  Z  O  L  C  M  K  E  J  T
```

BATS	BUDGERIGAR	BULLFINCHES
GLORIA	HOBBY	MUNTJAC
NUTHATCH	RABBIT	SLOWWORM
TAWNYOWL	VOLE	WOODPECKER

THE FOX AND THE FRIENDSHIP

'Do you think he needs something to eat?'
'Of course he does ... Look at him! ... Poor little mite,' was
the swift reply.

May Letter – "The Fox And The Friendship"

(EXTRACT FROM THE STORY)

"... he was now in great danger of dying a horrible and painful death... Blood stained and limping he pushed through the laurel hedge."

To The Family

Dear Kids

Thanks for keeping in touch with all your news. I was very interested and excited to hear that there may be fox cubs living near your garden. It's true to say there are many fox families to be seen at the moment, both in towns and countryside. Most of the cubs are probably only six or so weeks old, and if you do see them it indicates their home, called an *earth* or *den*, will be close by. Keep watching!

Well, after the drama in my last letter and all this talk about foxes, I thought a story about a fox in our garden might be well-timed, but we've never had cubs visit us as far as I know.

This is a story that took place over a three-month period some 10 years ago and happened almost entirely in our front garden, which, as you know is not very big and is overlooked by four other townhouses.

"Our Little..."

One evening, when coming back from work, I drove my noisy old car into the driveway. This was no different from any other weekday as I pulled to a standstill, turned off the engine and radio, and started to wind up the window. It was then I noticed a little brown face peeking out from our dense laurel hedge. Almost straight away I realised what it was; a young fox. Slowly, I opened the door and got out of the car. The face retreated back into the hedge. Now at this point, I fully expected the fox to run off, but it didn't. It sat there, obviously thinking it was well hidden, which it was. I pretended not to look at it as I walked to the front door and went inside.

'You'll never guess what I've just seen,' I said to Auntie Bridget. 'A fox out at this time of day, and it's still sitting in the hedge.'

'Where?' Auntie B asked in a disbelieving voice.

We both peered out of the window, but the fox was nowhere to be seen.

'You're dreaming .... Always dreaming.' said Auntie B.

Well, I thought no more of it until I returned home the next evening to be met by the same face, in the same place. Only this time it wasn't just a face, there was a complete head and neck, poking out from the laurel. I followed the same routine as the day before; engine off; window closed; walked to the front door ... you know what I mean. But this time I tried to engage the "fox-head" in polite conversation.

'Good Evening, and how are you today?'

Not surprisingly I got no reply, but the "head" remained poking out of the hedge as the fox followed my progress to the front door.

Did it have a body I wondered?

'It's out there again,' I said to Auntie Bridget.

'What's out there?' Auntie B replied as she busied herself in the kitchen

'*The fox*, of course,' I retorted, and with a sceptical, deep sigh Auntie Bridget moved to the window .... *No Fox ... again!*

'I think you need your eyes tested. You really shouldn't be driving, you know,' was her flippant reply.

Well, I'm not going to bore you with yet more repetition, but only to say my conversations with the fox became a little longer and the fox became a little bolder as time went on.

Then, on my return one evening, there it was, lying asleep in a tight, neat ball near the centre of the front lawn. I felt as if I should have crept passed, but as I got out of the car the fox woke up. It raised its head, yawned and looked at me as if to say, "you're late," and promptly rested its chin down onto an extended front paw. As I got inside, I was met by Auntie Bridget who said the fox had been sleeping there for about half an hour.

Now, you may have noticed I keep referring to the fox as "It" because, up to this point, I didn't know if "It" was a "He" or a "She". I needed Auntie B to confirm "It" was, in fact, a "HE", and Auntie Bridget made the fatal mistake of naming "him"... "Our Little Boy", or "OLB" for short.

OLB was small, and I guessed probably about fifteen months old. He had a beautiful golden-brown coat with a gleaming off-white

Colour me in!

bib of fur that stretched from his tummy up to and over his muzzle, making him look a little like a highwayman. His tail was bushy, long and in a magnificently flowing condition. His ears were pointed and soft-looking, and his eyes were dark and alert. OLB was certainly a handsome young fellow.

Now, I have to confess, in the past, I've sometimes been naughty, especially when I was a boy. Yes, I used to pick my nose in public; yes, I used to burp at the dinner table; yes, I used to *"Trouser Burp"* whilst watching the television - still do if I'm honest and always blame it on Holly Dog. And *yes*, I *did* pull Zoe's hair, run off, and blamed it on one of her brothers.

And, even though I'm a little older ... I also have to admit to being naughty for feeding "Our Little Boy". Eeeek!

In my defence, it was quite a long time ago, and now we understand our human relationship with urban foxes has changed. I quite understand that some folks don't like foxes, in town or in the countryside, and I'm NOT going to write this letter to take one side or another in the argument for liking or disliking foxes.

Well, the feeding started that very evening when he was sitting, head in hands, or should I say head on paws. *And I blame Auntie Bridget* because she happened to have some old bacon in the fridge, which had been left over from the previous weekend.

'Auntie B, do you think he's looking a little thin?' I mistakenly asked.

'Yes!' she replied with concern in her voice

'Do you think he needs something to eat?'

'Of course he does ... Look at him ... poor little mite,' was the swift reply.

.... See, I told you! It was ALL Auntie B's fault that we started to feed OLB.
With that, out came the bacon and out went I to place three cut-up rashers of bacon on the path, just outside the front door. Well, it took about a millisecond for OLB to jump up, run over and eat the free offerings.

'Oh, he's so hungry, poor little thing,' said Auntie Bridget. More food was delivered to the path with the same response from OLB.

Now, you can guess the rest because every evening OLB would be sleeping in the garden and only awoke when he heard my noisy old car coming up the road.

The menu was upgraded from "out of date bacon", via pork sausages, to best cuts of finest chicken breast, procured from the local butcher.

On one occasion, OLB was given my supper because he was "Looking *so* hungry," according to Auntie B.

'Well, what *am I* going to eat?'

'Oh, I think you'll find some *old, out of date bacon* somewhere at the back of the fridge. It's only been open for a week or two. It *should* be alright,' Auntie Bridget replied as she gazed lovingly at the fox.

'...Ummm,' I thought. 'So when's OLB moving into the house then?' I said sarcastically.

'When you move out!'

As the days passed into weeks, both OLB and I grew more confident in each other's company. I would sit on the front lawn, reading a book or drinking a cup of tea and eating a crumpet, and he slept next to me. If I did a little gardening, he would peer over to see what was going on, occasionally nodding his approval.

'Should I cut this rose back a little?' I pointed and asked him. 'What do you think my little friend?'

I took his relaxed sigh as confirmation I was making the right decision by trimming the plant.

Now, I've thought long and hard as to whether I should tell you just how naughty I was, and decided I would ... If Auntie B and I were having supper or a barbeque outside I would feed OLB by hand, just as you might give a pet dog a treat ... Unlike our Holly Dog, who just snatches the treats, OLB was so gentle every time he took a piece of meat from between my forefinger and thumb. It was an experience I will never forget, BUT it is also something we should never do again. Foxes can bite, and that's not good, but also it's not fair on the fox for the following, very important, reason. Foxes should *never* feel they can trust people because simply they can't. Foxes cannot tell the difference between people who can get along with them and people who can't, and that will place them in big trouble. It's not fair on the fox or those people who have reason not to like them. We should resist feeding foxes, if possible, and never by hand.

See ... I told you I was naughty!

Sometimes, if we were a little late in providing dinner, OLB would tap on the patio glass doors in our kitchen with his front paw, much to the annoyance of Holly Dog. She would bark and bark, but it never seemed to put him off. When I took OLB his "best cut of beef" supper Holly Dog sometimes looked at me as if to say:

'What's he done to deserve this treatment? All I get is a crummy plate of dog food. And, whilst I'm having a moan and groan, why does he get "seconds" of chicken breast?'

I would reply by saying: "This world can be so unfair, Holly Dog," as I poured on an extra portion of his favourite gravy. She's never quite forgiven me.

Some six weeks after meeting OLB for the first time, I arrived home somewhat later than usual and found Auntie Bridget in the garden with a distressed and anxious look on her face. She was at one end of the lawn and OLB at the other.

'There's something not right,' said Auntie Bridget worriedly. 'I think he's got caught in some barbed wire.'

OLB allowed me to get a little closer, but not as close as normal before he ran off into the hedge with the wire trailing behind him.

'That's not barbed wire,' I said, 'It's a wire "*snare*" trap'.

At some stage in the day, OLB must have passed through a hedge where somebody had set a trap using a circle of thick wire. This wire would normally be tied to a nearby tree in the hope of catching and killing a rabbit or fox, when the loop of wire tightened around the unsuspecting animal.

OLB had this trap caught around his middle, and as he had pulled, in a desperate attempt to escape, the wire had cut into his body. But at least he had been able to break away from the tree or post that had secured the wire. However, he was now in great danger of dying a horrible and painful death.

Next day we spoke to the RSPCA, who gave us a cage to see if we could catch him when he returned for his dinner that evening.

Well, he did return. Bloodstained and limping he pushed through the laurel hedge, but no matter how hard I tried to entice him into the cage with chicken pieces he wouldn't go in it. Slowly, he turned

Colour me in!

away from me and without eating he crawled back under the hedge and disappeared with the wire still tightly cutting into him.

Our worry and concerns got worse when he didn't come back to us the following evening.

As each day passed, I would do a little gardening in the hope I might see OLB, and if I heard a noise in the laurel bush, I'd look up in case it was him. I missed our little boy and felt guilty that maybe I could have done more to help on that first evening. Our hopes were fading that we would ever see OLB again.

***

Three days followed without a visit, but early one evening a moving shadow appeared at the top of our *back* lawn. It was difficult to make out exactly what it was, but the shadow moved quickly passed the flowerbeds, down the steps and to the closed patio glass doors. "*Tap, Tap ... Tap, Tap*". I could now see the outline of a familiar shape.

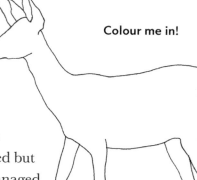

Colour me in!

It was OLB ... He'd returned!

'He's back! , he's back!' I exclaimed to Auntie Bridget. Not only had he returned but the wire was gone. Somehow he had managed to get free from the trap, probably by biting it off.

106

Whilst I went outside to greet him Auntie Bridget rushed to the fridge and quickly prepared his favourite dinner of chicken fillet. He wolfed it down, or should I say "Foxed" it down, in seconds. Our relief was only matched by the excitement we felt at seeing him again.

That evening, OLB stayed with us until it was completely dark. As I flicked on the outside patio light, he decided it was time for his night adventures to begin. Without a backward glance, he turned and made his way up the steps and onto the lawn. Running to the top of the garden, he stopped, looked back at us as if to offer his thanks, before melting into the darkness.

Over the following weeks, OLB's injuries slowly healed and normal dinner service was resumed, but that wasn't the end of the story, because OLB was joined on his daily visits to our front garden by a friend ... not another fox, but a female roe deer. Both would explore the garden together. Often he would fall asleep in his usual place on the lawn, and she would gently push him with her nose in a successful attempt to wake him up. This daily event took place for over a week. A strange, but touching and beautiful friendship.

The last time we saw OLB was three months after our first introduction. I spotted him chasing another fox around the front garden. Both ran through the hedge and away into the distance.

I often hear the foxes calling and barking at night, especially in the winter months, and I always think and hope they are the children of Our Little Boy.

***

I hope you enjoyed this story of garden friendship. On the next page, you will find some interesting facts about foxes along with a story related letter mix-up.

Well, you've just read about my naughty behaviour, so I thought in my next letter I'd write about animal bad behaviour in the garden and the "Big Beast Egg Thieves".

Keep looking in your garden or park and let me know what you see, maybe draw a picture.

Kindest Regards,
Uncle Steve

A Strange "Garden Friendship"

THE FOX AND THE FRIENDSHIP ACTIVITIES

Which ONE of the following facts is TRUE?

- Foxes' front paws each have five digits (or toes). However, they have only four on their hind, or back paws
- Foxes have a maximum speed of 25mph
- Female foxes, called vixens, normally have two families a year –Foxes live in homes called lodges.
- Red Foxes aren't found in Australia

The Fox and the Friendship Activities Page
See if you can unscramble the words from the below

Created on TheTeachersCorner.net Scramble Maker

1. IrLuea egedH	Where did I first see the fox's head?
2. urO Ltelti yBo	What name did we call the fox?
3. gywnmHhaai	Who or what did we think the fox looked like?
4. oBcna	What type of meat did we first give to the fox?
5. uaSassge	What else did we feed to the fox?
6. IlyoH goD	Who got annoyed with the fox?
7. inG Tapr	What did the fox get caught in?
8. PSACR	Who gave us a cage?
9. Reo eDer	What type of animal became friends with the fox?

The answers can be found at the back of the book on page 238

ANIMALS BEHAVING BADLY - IN THE GARDEN

"In the bright sunlight, its wings, with a wingspan longer than you are tall, shone as if covered with oil or wax, and its wingtip feathers were splayed-out like a Parisian fan."

June Letter –
"Animals behaving badly - In the Garden"
(EXTRACT FROM THE STORY)

"Are you telling me you ' cooked a grass snake in ...

MY OVEN?" Auntie B sharply questioned.

To The Family

Dear Kids

I hope you are all well and not missing seeing and playing with all your friends too much. This really is a beastly and annoying time for so many people.

Talking about *"annoying things"*, Holly Dog has stolen Auntie Bridget's first tomatoes of the season, and two, huge garden visitors have been stealing eggs; more about them later. Even Auntie B's been getting in on the act as I'm pretty sure she stole a chocolate bar I'd hidden in a kitchen drawer.

'Auntie Bridget, have you seen my Twix? I'm sure I left it in this drawer; you know the one by the hob.'

'*Nope*, don't think so. You probably ate it and have just forgotten.'

Now, Auntie B often blames me, like this, when actually she is at fault.

'Are you *absolutely* sure?' I pressed.

'Well, I *might* have had just a little ...'

I'd heard enough. Whatever next!
To make things worse, it's raining here
today, so I thought it may be a great time to
write to you about other mischievous things
that have been happening in my garden. I've
been wondering if you've had any naughty
animals or annoying insects visiting you in your garden or local park;
maybe a wasp or mosquitoes?

Firstly, I must apologise if I interrupt this letter from time to time
as I have to jump up from my desk, run outside and chase off some
naughty woodpigeons that enjoy eating the wild flower seed I've just
put down on my lawn. I've told them:
'If you keep munching away at MY seed I'll send Holly Dog out to
munch away at you!'

Yet more bad behaviour, in my view of things. They must know
I'm bluffing because the devils keep coming back, and Holly Dog
has no interest in chasing them; she thinks I'm quite mad. I thought
you might be interested to know that, just the other day, I found a
complete blackbird's egg in the middle of my flower bed, but I've
no idea how it got there. It's possible that one of the parents threw
it away if it refused to hatch. However, it may be that the egg was
stolen by another bird, which just fancied a boiled egg for breakfast,
but then thought better of it and dropped the egg in the garden. See,
I told you, everybody is behaving badly; except for you and me, of
course.

Well, I took the egg inside and somehow it got broken, causing
a mess and nasty smell. Clearly, it was very old, and Auntie B was

none too pleased with me.

'I told you not to bring it inside. It's been three days now, and I can still smell it,' she said angrily.

'And, by the way,' she added, 'where did you put that dead grass snake you found? It had better be in your shed because there's another ghastly odour in the kitchen.'

I now recalled I'd placed the snake in an old shoebox and hidden it in one of the kitchen cupboards, just under the sink ... I had to think of an excuse, and quickly.

'It's fine, I'm sure I put it outside, somewhere,' I lied, thinking I could quickly move the snake out of the kitchen when Auntie B left the room.

'Yep, I remember now, I took it to the log-store, just after drying it out in the oven yesterday.'

'You did WHAT!" Oh dear, this wasn't going well. "Are you telling me you 'cooked' a grass snake in ... MY OVEN?' Auntie B snapped.

'Well, I wouldn't quite say "cooked it", exactly, more like warmed it up,' I replied, somewhat defensively.

I hardly need to tell you that the conversation wasn't going to plan, and Auntie Bridget was by now, literally, fuming. Things were only set to get worse, and to this day, I can't really understand why.

I offered up this helpful comparison in my defence:

'I can't actually see the difference between heating up the snake, to dry it out, and cooking a chicken for Sunday lunch.'

With one hand resting on her hip, and the forefinger of the other pointing, no, prodding at me, she ordered:

'That's it! ... I've had enough; NO MORE dead animals in this house; NO MORE bones; NO MORE birds' wings; NO MORE snakes and NO MORE dead beetles.'

Auntie B was sounding just like my mother had, when, as a boy, I brought the grass snake home in the birdcage.

'Is there anything else you've hidden in the house without telling me?' she asked, crossly.

Then, as I thought to myself, should I tell her about the live maggots I use for fishing, that I was keeping in the bottom of the fridge; especially as a few had escaped from their box overnight to roam the salad shelf? After all, I'd gathered up most of them and given each a telling off. No, maybe it wasn't a good time to break this interesting but unfortunate bit of news to her; maybe later.

***

Well, over the past weeks, the sun has shone and nature's been busily preparing for late spring and early summer. Butterflies are flitting here and there, but never really making up their minds as to where, exactly, they want to land. Birds are tweeting, and the longest day of the year has just passed.

Each morning, before dawn, I'm woken by an annoyingly noisy and tweety Song Thrush, who, it would seem, feels the need to wake everybody up before the sun rises. This reminds me of when I was your age; my mother would also annoyingly wake me up far too early for school.

'Stephen,' she would say abruptly. 'Stephen, get up ... now! If you stay in that bed any longer you'll grow

Colour me in!

roots, like a potato.'

I would then check under my bed-sheets ... NO roots, just a pair of very sleepy legs that understandably, in my view, refused to move.

'You're going to be late again,' she would say as I raced down to breakfast. 'And look at you! Your shoelaces are undone; your shirt; your tie; your hair; all undone ... You're a completely, untidy mess Stephen'.

'What else have you left undone, Young Man?'

'My homework!' I whispered under my breath.

Well, not a lot has changed after all these years. My legs are still sleepy in the early hours of the day, and my hair's still "undone", but at least I don't have any homework to finish when the thrush wakes me up at four o'clock in the morning. Mummies, daddies, and birds can be so annoying first thing in the morning; don't you think?

Excuse me for a moment as the pigeons are back, so I need to rush outside and chase them off, yet again.

That's better. I've just run two laps of the garden, clapping my hands and shouting:

"Get away you Blighters or I'll set Holly Dog onto you."

I have no idea what the neighbours think of my pigeon-chasing, but I can guess.

As I return to my study and look out of the window, I can see all four pigeons are sitting and waiting in a distant beech tree. I'm pretty sure they're laughing at me.

'Little Devils!' I say to Holly Dog, who's still lying on her comfy sofa next to me.

Well, it's not only the aggravating thrush and thieving pigeons that have been busy in the garden as lots more "bad behaviour" has been taking place.

Great spotted woodpeckers are fighting each other for space on Auntie B's coconut bird feeders, and the blackbirds have been squabbling amongst themselves about everything, from which of them can perch, and poop, on my garden chair, to who's going to eat an unfortunate worm that's just appeared on the lawn.

Talking of poo, we even have a pair of pooping collared doves nesting over our front porch; I can report mother and eggs are doing well but the mess on the doorstep is so annoying.

But the big news is that we've had *Egg Stealers* raiding our magpies' nest, which is right at the top of our Scott's pine tree, so read on to find out more.

The Beast from The Sky

Please forgive me if I tell you a little about the thieves and when I first saw them. They're a species of Big Bird never seen in our garden before. In fact, I've only ever spotted this bird in the wild once in my life, exactly ten years ago.

I need to take you back a couple of weeks to when I saw one of the thieves for the first time. I was rambling, high on Hindhead Common, not far from our house, with Auntie Bridget and Holly Dog when we were approached by a boy walking with his spaniel. He saw I had a pair of binoculars hanging around my neck and asked if I'd seen a big bird, flying high in the sky, being attacked by two smaller, black coloured birds. Right on cue, all three birds appeared in full flight from behind a scattering of pine trees, and they were still squabbling amongst themselves about whose aerial display was best. I was sure the two smaller birds were crows and they were chasing off a big eagle-like bird called a buzzard. I'd seen our garden crows in similar combat with buzzards, high above our house, so I was confident I was right.

But I was wrong, or at least partly wrong. Yes, the two smaller birds were crows, and they were chasing off the much bigger bird ... but it wasn't a buzzard. This big bird was jet black with long wings; a large head and a massively powerful "mallet-like" beak. In the bright sunlight, its wings, with a wingspan longer than you are tall, shone as if covered with oil or wax, and its wingtip feathers were splayed-out like a Parisian fan.

The crows shouted out with a "Crah, Crah, Crah" ...and "Big Bird" replied with an angry, deep sounding "Clack ... Clack ... Caw", like the noise of a slowly turning football rattle.

High in the sky the threesome twisted and turned; ducked and dived. Both crows followed the acrobatic lead of their "avian*" enemy until all three dropped out of sight behind the ridge of a distant hill. (*Avian means "of birds")

Over the next three weeks, I saw two of these magnificent creatures on the common; always together.

Once, they both flew low over the pine trees at the top of our garden and were met by the full force of our crows, magpies and jackdaws. But even our entire "Garden Air Force" of birds

Colour me in!

was no match for this pair of marauders as they circled and swooped down overhead. After a minute or two, all of our birds scattered and dived into the trees for safety ... except for a single crow, who swerved from its steep descent and rose sharply upwards and above the two intruders. There, our heroic crow repeatedly dropped down, almost crashing into each Big Bird in turn. Eventually, his or her, incredible bravery forced both invaders to flee. I was so proud.

"That's My Boy ... or Girl!" I said to myself.

Even then, I felt the intruders were simply testing our garden defences ... and on this occasion, I was to be proved right.

As you know, I'm getting rather old and very forgetful, so you may be thinking:

'Old Uncle Steve's forgotten to tell us the name of these Big Birds.'

Well, I haven't forgotten! ... I just wanted you to guess the identity of these huge, shiny, jet black birds with a wingspan longer than you are tall ... What do you think? ... I'll give you a clue. Some members of this species of bird live within the walls of The Tower of London, and it's said that "if they were ever to leave, our Kingdom would fall". These are birds of legend and dark mystery.

Okay, I'll tell you ... it was a Raven, or more to the point, two Ravens! Well done if you guessed correctly.

Ravens, crows, rooks, magpies, jackdaws and jays are all part of a bird family called Corvidae (but not Covid, the nasty disease). It's fair to say that most members of this strange, dysfunctional family don't get along with each other. I'm sure that's not the case in your family. And if you have brothers or sisters you never get angry or cross with each other! Um....

Ravens are quite rare but they can be seen nearby on the South Downs hills, and their population is slowly growing throughout our land, following hundreds of years of persecution by humans. Normally ravens live in faraway, craggy mountains, cliffs and ancient forests, but these two wild beasts have recently moved into our neighbourhood, near to Black Down.

Now, you might well be asking yourselves, with disappointment ... 'Is this the story?' and thinking 'What happened about the egg-stealing?'

Well, I thought no more about the rampaging ravens until a couple of days ago when I heard that now familiar deep "Clack ... Clack" raven call in the distance. Unable to see them, I grabbed my binoculars and climbed up to the lower branches of a sycamore tree to observe just what was going on.

There they were; the two ravens, hiding near the top of a pine tree, about 50 metres away. Their heads were close to each other in deep discussion; as if putting together a secret plan. After an agreement was reached, they said their "goodbyes" and moved apart. Then, one of the ravens flew between two of our neighbours' houses and up towards the top of the Scots pine tree, where the magpies have their nest. Despite one of the magpies being on the "lookout" from a nearby fir tree and the other perching close to the nest, both were surprised at the arrival of this massive, flying beast.

I couldn't see exactly what happened next because a magpie nest is both deep and normally quite well protected with thorny twigs, but both magpies scattered as this raven grabbed at least one egg with its huge beak. The magpies, still shocked, let out panic cries, then, together managed to chase the raven from the nest. As all three flew away over the rooftops, the second raven flew low across our garden and up to the nest, I guess, gobbling yet more eggs.

All this noise and commotion drew the attention of the crows, which finally took to the air to investigate what was happening. By then the thieves were flying separately into the distance.

A few minutes later, after the magpies had returned, one of the ravens was back, looking for more nests to raid. This time our Garden Air Force was ready and waiting. Up they all went, and a sky battle took place with the single raven being mobbed by not just the magpies but also our two crows. The war continued as the single raven was chased off and flew away, acrobatically swerving from side to side under the attack.

Now, you might think, "how foolish of the raven to return alone and so soon." Let me tell you, ravens are NOT stupid! I was also surprised to see the raven was actually flying away quite slowly, albeit the aerial combat was furious.

It was then I realised just how clever these ravens are, because as all of our Garden Air Force was at war with the first raven, I saw the low, quiet approach of the second raven from the opposite direction. Unchallenged, this raven firstly visited the magpie nest before flying across the garden to the crows' nest and possibly stealing one of their eggs. It was all part of a "Raven Master Plan"; a double attack.

Well, to outsmart two magpies and two crows, all of whom are super smart, was quite some feat. I felt a little sad that our garden birds had lost at least some of their eggs, especially as magpies usually have only one clutch of eggs a year. But, all Corvids, including magpies, steal eggs and chicks from other birds' nests. My brother, Nick, caught a single crow stealing five eggs from his chickens, within just a few minutes.

It was quite exciting to see these huge birds visiting our garden, even if they were thieves and vagabonds. All that said, it's probably best if the ravens don't return to our garden again this year, at least until the chicks have left the nest. We'll wait and see if any magpie chicks fledge the nest this year and I'll let you know what happens ... Phew, what excitement!

***

Caught In the Tree

I'd previously mentioned that I had been watching all of this exciting activity from the branches of a sycamore tree. Now, I'm not quite as young as I used to be, and one of the things about getting old is that it's easier climbing UP trees than it is climbing DOWN, and I only remembered this whilst sitting IN the sycamore.

Well, after two unsuccessful attempts to get down from my uncomfortable perch, I had the bright idea of using my mobile phone to telephone Auntie Bridget:

"'Brrr, Brrr,' the phone went ... No reply!

'Please leave a message after the tone ... Beeeep,' said the recorded message

'Oh, blast!' I cursed to myself, but I didn't leave a message.

'Ah, I know, I'll phone my neighbour, David, and ask him to bring his step-ladder'.

'Brr ... Brr,' the phone rang,

'"Hello,' David answered.

'Hi David. It's Stephen, from next door; I'm in a spot of bother.'

'Are you okay? Is it the virus? Shall I call an Ambulance?'

'No. No, nothing like that ... It's ... actually it's a bit embarrassing,' I sheepishly replied. 'I'm, err, stuck up a tree, with my binoculars ... bird watching!'

'What ... Up a tree, bird watching ... at your age? Are you sure you're not spying on your neighbours?' He laughed. 'I'll be right out ... with a camera!'

'I'd prefer you bring a step-ladder,' I pleaded.

By this time Auntie Bridget had seen my "missed call" on her mobile phone, and thinking I had had an accident (why else would I be phoning her from the garden?) had rushed outside to see if I was okay.

'What the Devil do you think you are doing up that tree with a pair of binoculars?' This wasn't a question from Auntie B, but more of an exasperated statement.

'What will the neighbours think if they see you?' .... This was a question. 'You're 63 years old, and you're still climbing trees!'

'I was just watching these birds......' I started.

Auntie Bridget interrupted. 'Stop! ... Stop right now ... Thank goodness the neighbours haven't seen you. Get down from that tree at once!'

'Errrr, actually, errrm, I've just phoned David for a helping hand,' I replied from my lofty branch.

'Oh no,' Auntie Bridget sighed, and for a moment, put her face in both hands. 'Just look at you, stuck up a tree: You look a mess; you've

still got your slippers on; your flies are undone; your shirt's undone
.......' Auntie B sounded just like my mother, all those years ago.

'You know, nothing really changes, even after 50 years,' I whispered
to myself. 'I'm still always getting into trouble and annoying Auntie B.'

Just as I thought life couldn't get any worse, David and his wife,
along with other neighbours, arrived to poke more fun at me.

'So where's your tree-house, Tarzan?' David teased, much to the
merriment of the others.

You see, it's not only my Garden Family that can be annoying at
this time of year ... But at least David brought a ladder.

***

**I hope you enjoyed this little story about bad behaviour,
and now for a bit of good news**: I'm really pleased to report that
Gloria has been spotted. I know this because I heard my neighbour,
Susan, screaming "Snake! ... *Big Snaaake!*" whilst jumping up and
onto her garden table in terror...

'Good Old Gloria; up to her usual tricks,' I chuckled.

Well, the rain has stopped, and I can hardly believe it but those
naughty woodpigeons are back again to eat my wild flower seed. So,
you know what I've got to do. This is like a Joe Wicks workout.

Keep looking in your garden at all your beautiful creatures; great,
small, and tiny.

The Very Best of Regards,
Uncle Steve

Ravens never follow the rules!

ANIMALS BEHAVING BADLY ACTIVITIES

Raven – Which ONE statement is TRUE?

• Ravens lay their eggs in April
• Adult ravens have a wingspan of just under one metre
• Ravens can fly upside down for short distances
• Ravens are Raptors
• Ravens are in the same "Bird Family" as Blackbirds

HOW TO MAKE AUNTIE B'S SEED 'N SUET MIX RECIPE (AUTUMN, WINTER & SPRING)

Ingredients – 250 g lard and 200g peanut butter
Dry ingredients made up to 900 g to include packet of beef suet, breadcrumbs, sugar, grated apple, currants, raisins, mixed bird seed.

Melt lard and peanut butter in pan over heat. Add all the dry ingredients and mix together well. Put in storage containers and allow to set in cool place or fridge.

When ready, spoon out in suitable bird feeders. Auntie B uses half coconuts from pet shops hung up with string. You can make a feeder by cutting in half a recycled plastic bottle, make a hole in the side wall of the bottle and feed through a length of strong string and knot it like you would a conker on a string.

See which birds eat on the feeder and those that feed underneath, on the ground.

The recipe above is not suitable for summer feeding, when protein is needed.

The answers can be found at the back of the book on page 239

HOUSE GUESTS

"How did Miss Jackdaw do that?"

July Letter – "House Guests"

(EXTRACT FROM THE STORY)

"That's Molly Mouse, my Pilates Pal ... surely you've met."

To The Family

Dear Kids

In my last letter, we discovered lots of bad behaviour going on outside. Well, there has also been plenty of naughtiness and strange things happening *inside* the house over the past couple of months, and I thought you would like to hear about them.

Only last week, one of my old friends told me that a big grass snake, obviously a friend of Gloria, slithered *into* their kitchen, using the cat-flap as her entrance. After a lot of panics and hysterical screaming, "Gladys", as I've called her, was popped into a box, taken to the bottom of the garden and returned to the vegetation next to their pond. What great fun!

Now, with this annoying lockdown, you might think that nobody is allowed to visit us at the moment, except for the usual spiders, flies and of course grass snakes, but some of our garden creatures just don't follow the rules. As most of them actually live in the garden I guess they won't get told off ... *except by me.*

So, this letter contains four little stories that have taken place *in* our home.

House Guests

The first is about a magpie that invites himself to lunch. This is followed by a mouse enjoying morning exercise classes. Then there's a story of a very young blackbird, seemingly wanting to take a shower. And finally, we have a woodpigeon that insists on doing the washing-up.

***

"Magpie or Chicken Pie for Lunch?" – The Uninvited Diner

You may remember from my last letter that our magpie couple had recently lost their eggs to those crafty ravens. Well, that means both magpies have a little too much time on their hands at the moment, which has led them to get up to all kinds of mischief.

Firstly, they are chasing any blackbird that dares to land on our back lawn. The blackbirds fly under, over, through and behind bushes and trees, closely followed by one of the magpies. This chase only stops when the blackbird scampers out of the garden. But the blackbird doesn't seem bothered as it darts straight back over the hedge to continue the search for worms amongst the grass and flowerbeds. This *backwards and forwards* game can go on for as much as half an hour until the magpies find somebody else to annoy.

The magpies' next target is a single jackdaw that flies in from our neighbour's garden to raid Auntie Bridget's coconut bird feeder. Mr Magpie isn't going to allow that kind of behaviour in HIS garden ... Oh

NO! So after "Miss Jackdaw" has precariously hung and flapped from the bottom of the coconut feeder and quickly snatched a *beak-full* of Auntie B's special lunch mix of seed and suet, another chase takes place and Miss Jackdaw is *escorted* from the garden. But she, like the blackbird returns only minutes later for a second acrobatic food grab.

You will have noticed I refer to our neighbour's jackdaw as Miss Jackdaw, but I have to admit I don't actually know if this bird is a boy or a girl. What I can say is that the jackdaw has a particularly beautiful, dark and light grey headscarf of feathers, which would grace any Paris fashion show, and "she" always comes into our garden alone. Male jackdaws often have a more silvery coloured hoodie.

In any case, once Miss Jackdaw is well on her way, the magpie returns to the coconut to try and figure out how Miss Jackdaw performed the trick of getting her lunch from the feeder. Mr Magpie tips his head to one side, whilst peering up at the coconut as if to say "How did Miss Jackdaw do that?" Mr Magpie will then fly to each of our coconut feeders in turn as if looking for the answer ... always without success. Sometimes he will fly up to the coconut and attempt to dislodge a chunk of food by attacking it with a combination of pecking and wing beats. But when this doesn't work, he gets so cross, squawks at the coconut and then flaps and hops about in a frenzy of frustration. I'd call it a tantrum, from a bird that's got a very bad attitude problem at the moment.Now, you may be wondering what this has got to do with Mr Magpie inviting himself to lunch.

Well, the other day, just after Auntie B had filled each of the coconuts with her magic food mix, she returned inside our house and put the food mixing bowl on our dining room table as she always does. This daily routine hadn't gone unnoticed. As I've said before, all Corvids, including magpies, are very bright, and despite not being able to hang upside down from the bottom of the coconut, like Miss Jackdaw, Mr Magpie was still keen to feast on Auntie B's delicious dinner.

That day, quite by chance, I had decided to have a spot of light lunch whilst sitting at the dining room table and reading the newspaper. I sat at one end of the table and Auntie B's "Seed and Suet" was at the other. After a few minutes of enjoying a small slice of chicken pie and the first half of my extremely delicious cheese and pickle sandwich, I heard a light scurrying sound on the floor and assumed Holly Dog had joined me for a lunchtime treat of sandwich crust. I leaned over the arm of my chair and looked under the table for her.

'Funny,' I thought, as she was nowhere to be seen.

'I must have imagined the noise,' I said to myself as I set about reading the newspaper.

Then more scurrying ... more peering under the table, but still no Holly Dog.

As I raised my head for the second time I was met by Mr Magpie, elegantly dressed in his black and white dinner suit, "sitting" at the other end of the table and tucking into Auntie B's magic mix... but he wasn't using a napkin or a knife and fork!

'Where are your table manners?' I whispered.

With that, he hopped off the table, onto the floor and then flew back out of the open patio doors.

I went to the kitchen to tell Auntie Bridget what had happened, and to get a drink.

'Not another one of your tall stories,' Auntie B sighed.

'Honest, he was sitting at the opposite end of the table, having lunch with me,' I slightly exaggerated. 'We discussed the weather and how good your "Seed and Suet Mix" tasted'.

Auntie Bridget didn't reply, just tutted and muttered to herself.

'Uncle S, you really do need to get out more.'

Orange squash in hand, I returned to the dining room to finish the second half of my delicious sandwich and final small piece of chicken pie, only to find both had mysteriously disappeared.

'Now, where's the rest of my lunch gone? Maybe I finished it and just forgot. Well, I'm getting rather old and forgetful,' I mused. 'I know, it's that naughty, thieving Holly Dog.'

Even at her age of fourteen and a half, she's rather partial to stealing from low lying plates of food.

It was then I happened to look out of the window and saw the remains of my lovely sandwich on the lawn being gobbled up by both Mr and Mrs Magpie.

Clearly, he'd returned when I left the room, hopped or flew to my end of the table and stole the rest of my lunch. Magpies have a reputation for being thieves, just like Holly Dog, and this proved it.

'Typical! And, he didn't even say "goodbye", or, "thanks for Lunch" ... MY LUNCH. I bet Miss Jackdaw would've been more polite,' I complained.

Since then Auntie B has seen him regularly hopping through the open patio doors at about 12.30 in search of a free lunch - with or without an invitation.

"There's a Mouse in the House"

Often I hear mice scampering and scratching around in our loft, and in the past, I've put traps up there to catch them alive, before releasing the little blighters into the woods at the top of the garden. Sometimes, I've even transported them in my car to a nearby field. Auntie Bridget believes I'm quite mad and says the mice get back to the house quicker than I do: she could be right!

Well, it's not just me who has a soft spot for our "furry friends". Just the other day, I thought I heard Auntie B talking to somebody, whilst doing her daily stretches and exercises in our bedroom.

We have two glass doors that open onto an outside, first-floor balcony, with decking below and one of Auntie B's coconut bird feeders hanging from the gutter above. Auntie Bridget always does her online exercise class with these bedroom balcony doors wide open. Much of the food pecked off the feeder by the coal tits, woodpeckers and Miss Jackdaw falls to the balcony decking, where robins, blackbirds and other creatures prefer to dine.

Now, I'm banned from entering the room when this physical activity is underway, but normally I can hear uplifting music coming from our bedroom radio along with a lot of puffing and blowing, banging and groaning, coming from Auntie B. This is usually accompanied by the rather teacher-like voice of her "Online" Pilates instructor, giving directions like, "Breathe in ... and slowly breathe out". Now, I might be missing something but I think Auntie B learnt how to breathe just after she was born, 62 years ago, and unless she's just forgotten I'm pretty sure she doesn't need to be taught again.

'Next Auntie Bridget will be relearning how to count,' I whisper to myself with perfect timing, as through the crack in the door I hear her "teacher" instructing ... "One, two, threeee ... and *hold*.'

'I *think* "four" comes next, but I might be wrong,' I jokingly replied to myself.

Anyway, these "helpful" instructions are often followed by peculiarly named exercises like "The Plank" and "The Downward Dog"... It's all quite a mystery to me.

'Back to the story Uncle Steve,' I can hear you say.

Okay, I mentioned earlier that on one occasion Auntie B was also talking, which was most unusual.

'That's strange,' I thought; the music was still booming out of the room with the words – "*Let it go, let it go ... The cold never bothered me anyway*" - and in the background, her Pilates teacher was offering the usual life-changing advice about breathing and counting, so why was Auntie Bridget talking, rather than just blowing and groaning?

The conversation I overheard coming from Auntie B went something like this:

'Well my little friend, you need to stretch a little more and then hold that position a little longer'...

.... 'There's no way you can eat and exercise at the same time ... *now concentrate!*'

.... 'If you're going to run around like that, at least hop and skip to the music. Now, come along and sing with me ... "*That perfect girl has gone ... let the storm rage on,'*"... Auntie Bridget continued to sing.

At this point, I was thinking to myself 'Who the devil is Auntie Bridget talking to? These exercise classes have finally driven her quite mad.'

After the class had finished, Auntie Bridget eventually puffed her way downstairs and I naturally asked:

'Er... Good workout today then?'

'Yep ... not bad, but I'm a bit stiff,' Auntie B replied as she stretched at an awkward angle.

'Great! Anything interesting to tell me?'

'Nope, don't think so,' she replied and turned towards the fridge for a cold drink.

'Anybody else up there exercising with you?'

'Ooow, no, don't think so. Oh, except Molly of course,' she said, closing the refrigerator door.

'MOLLY! ... Who's Molly?'

'Molly lives outside; under the balcony decking ... Has done for weeks, by all accounts. Moved in after Easter.'

'WHAT... WHO?' I quizzed in amazement.

'Yes, she's been my exercise buddy since April.'

'Hold on a second; you have an exercise buddy who moved onto our balcony weeks ago, called Molly?' I must have sounded like an echo.

'That's about right. I've told you, she's my exercise buddy. Molly and I were thinking of nipping down to the coffee shop for a "Flat White", before going to the Gym. I need to get Molly a leotard and headband before our next exercise class.'

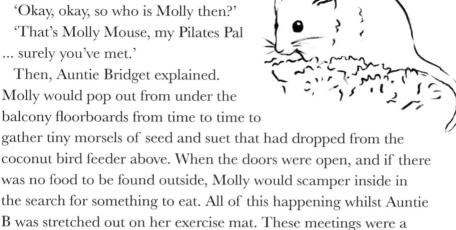

'Okay, okay, so who is Molly then?'
'That's Molly Mouse, my Pilates Pal
... surely you've met.'
Then, Auntie Bridget explained.
Molly would pop out from under the
balcony floorboards from time to time to
gather tiny morsels of seed and suet that had dropped from the
coconut bird feeder above. When the doors were open, and if there
was no food to be found outside, Molly would scamper inside in
the search for something to eat. All of this happening whilst Auntie
B was stretched out on her exercise mat. These meetings were a
regular occurrence to the point where both Molly and Auntie B were
now on "first name terms".

With that explanation, both Auntie Bridget and I went upstairs for
me to be formally introduced to our new housemate, but Molly was
nowhere to be found.

'Now it's you, Auntie Bridget, who needs to get out more,' I
jokingly insisted.

To this day I've never seen Molly, but I'll keep looking.

Blackbirds don't like baths; they prefer showers.
This is a very quick little story that Auntie Bridget told me, so it's
probably not true.

Just the other week, I mentioned to you about a robin that flew
into our bedroom, via the balcony doors, performed a couple of
aerial circuits around the room before flying back out through an
open window. Well, a similar encounter (that's a type of meeting)

happened yesterday involving Auntie B. But this time it was a young blackbird and not a robin that must have flown into our bedroom as Auntie Bridget was preparing to have a bath.

It's quite easy to identify a young blackbird that has just left the nest for the first time because they have no fear and don't yet know what to be frightened of. They often don't fly away when approached and peer at humans as if we're strange aliens from outer space. They also look different from their parents, as baby blackbirds have a shorter, stubby tail and frizzy, speckled, light brown breast feathers.

Well, Auntie B was settling down in her bubbly bath for a nice deep soak and "Sing Song" when who should enter the bathroom but the baby blackbird, hopping and scratching along the tiled floor.

Auntie B peeped over the side of the bath and saw the baby bird. At the same time, the baby bird looked up and saw Auntie B's head appear from over the top of the bath. I'm not sure who was the most surprised.

"How rude!" Auntie B exclaimed. "Just as I was getting comfortable."

Well, young "Beatrice Blackbird" found all this was very strange. "Why would anybody want to have a bubbly bath?" she probably thought.

Beatrice hopped around on the bathroom floor for a minute or two before deciding to inspect the shower cubicle in the corner, which seemed much more to her liking.

'You can't stay in there, Young Lady,' Auntie B stated.

Finally, Auntie Bridget got out of the bath and gently picked up Beatrice with both hands before taking her to the open window for release.

'Well, off you go now,' said Auntie Bridget.

Beatrice waited as if to say, 'Oh, is it time to leave already?' and then flapped her way over to our nearby cherry tree, where her anxious parents were waiting.

'I think you might get a bit of a telling off from your mum and dad, young Beatrice,' Auntie B whispered, before returning to relax in her bubbly bath.

Since then, we have seen Beatrice almost every day and she often hops onto the balcony and into the bedroom for a quick chat with Auntie B whilst pecking the decking for scraps of suet and seed mix. Beatrice and Auntie Bridget are getting on together famously.

"Where do you keep the washing-up liquid?"

Just the other evening, Auntie B and I were each drinking a lovely glass of lemonade and munching away at some crinkly crisps, whilst enjoying the last of the sun. Unusually, Holly Dog hadn't joined us.

'I wonder where she is,' Auntie Bridget said. 'Can you take a look inside? Oh, and whilst you're there; any chance of getting me a glass of chilled white wine?'

This was less of a question and more of an order from Auntie B.

So dutifully, I followed the instruction and trudged into the house, via the open patio doors, and through the sitting room to the hallway. There, on the carpet, was Holly Dog, fast asleep. I left her dozing and continued to the kitchen.

In just a minute, it will become clear to you why I have described my journey in such detail.

Well, on entering the kitchen I was met by a very tubby woodpigeon, standing on the worktop and peering into the sink as if doing the washing-up from tea.

It's fair to say both of us were surprised to see each other; I jumped back and Mrs Pigeon fluttered into the air with a mighty kerfuffle and a flapping of wings. In her panic, she flew around the room, banging and bashing into plates, mugs, cups and saucepans.

Whilst she was conducting her aerial tour of the kitchen, I reversed out of the room and gently closed the door behind me, before going back out to Auntie B with the news.

As I approached, Auntie Bridget seemed more concerned that I hadn't returned with her chilled wine than the exciting news of our kitchen visitor.

'The Bird can't stay in the kitchen, there'll be a mess everywhere ... You're good with birds and stuff, you sort it out,' Auntie B demanded. 'You've often been called around to the neighbours to catch birds, toads and snakes, so just get on with it!'

This was true, I had. On one occasion a hysterical lady had vigorously knocked on my front door and pleaded with me to remove: "A beastly bird from my sitting room, that's dropped down the chimney."

'Personally, I would have come in via the door,' I replied, but the lady was not amused.

'Auntie Bridget, I might need you to give me a hand with our kitchen pigeon.'

'Not on your life. I'm going nowhere near it. You sort it out; it's your problem. But, I'll come inside to make sure you don't create yet more of a mess'.

Even now I'm not sure why I was being blamed for the "bird break-in" and nor why I was being ordered to evict it.

As we went inside we found Holly Dog still asleep on the hall carpet, and, before opening the kitchen door, Auntie B raised this very interesting question:

'How did the pigeon get into the kitchen in the first place?'

Pigeons actually spend a lot of their time walking around looking for seeds and worms rather than flying. As the only way into the kitchen at that time was exactly as I described earlier, our pigeon friend must either have flown from room to room or "waddled" through the house, which I thought was more probable. So, if the pigeon had walked all the way to the kitchen it must have tiptoed right past, almost tripping over, the sleeping Holly Dog ... "Amazing!" I thought.

When I gave this insightful, yet complicated detail of the pigeon's journey to Auntie Bridget, I thought she would be as fascinated as I was. But she wasn't.

'You mean this darn bird has been strolling around my house as if he or she owns the place?'

'Well, yes, I guess so,' I concluded.

'Get IT OUT ... Right now!' came forth the order.

With that, I was pushed into the kitchen and the door was slammed behind me.

'Well Mrs Pigeon, where are you?' I asked quietly as I looked under the table and over to the far side of the room.

'Come out, come out wherever you are,' I sang, but "she" was nowhere to be seen.

I ventured a little further into the kitchen and had the feeling I was being watched in silence. She couldn't have got out, as the door and all the windows had been firmly closed.

It was only after a couple of minutes that our gazes met.

Whilst I was being "told off" in the hallway by Auntie B, our new resident had made herself very comfortable in one of our "upside-down", ceiling lampshades.

'What the devil is going on in there?' came the booming voice of Auntie Bridget from behind the still firmly closed kitchen door.

'She's made a "nest" in one of our lampshades,' I half-whispered in reply.

'WHAT! ... GET ... IT ... OUT!' The Voice demanded.

'But she looks so comfortable,' I jokingly informed Auntie B

"SHE! ... OUT, RIGHT NOW ... Do you hear - '

I still hadn't figured out exactly how I was to evict our house guest and I briefly considered asking Auntie B for advice ... but thought better of it.

In the kitchen, we have two glass doors that open out to a little garden patio. I realised this had to be the best route for our pigeon to leave the kitchen, but the problem was the patio doors were on the other side of the room and our new resident, as well as the kitchen table, was between me and the exit.

So, getting down on my hands and knees, I crawled between two kitchen chairs and under the table on my journey across the room.

At this point, Auntie B decided to slightly open the kitchen door, peering in to view my progress.

With dismay, she exclaimed, 'What on Earth do you think you're doing, crawling about on the floor? You are supposed to be a grownup. Stop playing around.' Then Auntie B started to laugh at the scene before her; a grown man on "all fours", bottom in the air, stuck under a table with a pigeon nesting and looking down from above.

'There really is no hope for you, Uncle Stephen.' Auntie Bridget laughed, sounding just like my mother once did.

Well, I crawled to the glass doors, stretched up and opened both of them before continuing to crawl into the garden. By the time I'd stood up and walked around the house and back into the hallway, I was surprised to hear Auntie B talking to the nesting pigeon.

'Okay Madam, time for you to leave.' I heard Auntie Bridget say. And with that, Mrs Pigeon took the advice and promptly flew out of the kitchen and into the garden.

Turning to me Auntie B said, 'Well Stephen, it took a woman to persuade my new pigeon girlfriend to leave. That's how you do it! And as I did your job, YOU, Stephen, can clear up all this mess'.

With that, Auntie B handed me a floor-cleaning mop and returned outside with her glass of chilled white wine to enjoy the evening sunshine.

***

I hope you have enjoyed these little stories about our garden family. Have you had any unusual house visitors, big or small? Maybe a spider or two?

Over the past nights we have had unseen garden guests. David, our neighbour has had all his flowers and vegetables nibbled, and we have collected some of their droppings for my sample tray. So which of our garden creatures has pooped The Poo? The answer is over the page.

Keep looking in your garden or local parks at all your beautiful animals and plants. You may see some flying ants over the next few days, leaving their nest to make new colonies.

You might have seen a *horsefly* but have you ever seen an ant-fly?

All my love,
Uncle Steve

P.S. – Just this morning, Mr Magpie walked into our bedroom, through the slightly open balcony doors, as bold as you like. He woke up both Auntie B and me with an almighty squawk as if ordering me to get out of bed and prepare breakfast. Maybe he was enquiring if I'd grown roots - just as my mother had all those years ago - and then he wandered back out and flew off cackling to himself. *The cheek of it!*

"Where is the Washing-up liquid?"

Not the best place to nest

HOUSE GUESTS ACTIVITIES

" The phantom Pooper was a roe deer."

JACKDAW FACTS (OR FICTION)
Which ONE Jackdaw statement below is FALSE?

- Jackdaws recognise individual human faces and expressions.
- The group or collective name for a gathering of Jackdaws is a Train, amongst other names.
- Jackdaws can have same-gender pairings.
- A Jackdaw in Rheims, France was, for a short time, made a saint.
- Jackdaws were once called "The Chimney Sweep" bird.

BLACKBIRD FACTS (OR FICTION)
Which ONE Blackbird statement below is TRUE?

- Blackbirds are members of the same family as crows, rooks, jackdaws and jays.
- Blackbirds, like crows, can have a combination of black and white feathers (excluding albinism).
- All UK, male blackbirds have yellow beaks.
- Iceland is the only European country to have no breeding pairs of Blackbirds.
- The first blackbirds to sing each year are mature males.

The answers can be found at the back of the book on page 241

House Guests Crossword

See if you can complete the House Guests Crossword below

Created using the Crossword Maker on TheTeachersCorner.net

Across

3. Who used the cat flap to get into the kitchen?
5. What animal did Auntie B exercise with?
6. What was the name of Auntie B's Bath time Buddie
7. Where do Blackbirds prefer to wash themselves

Down

1. Which type of bird invited himself to lunch?
2. What 'nested' in the lampshade?
4. What type of 'animal' exercise did Auntie B do?

145

THE BEAST OF EXMOOR

"CAUGHT! ...but not the Beast"

In the photo below, can you find the fish, called a
"Bullhead", from the story ... and identify what has caught it
- tail-first? You can just see the eye of the captive Bullhead
in the mouth of its captor.

"Was this really such a good idea to fish here?"

The name of the *captor* can be found on page 242 – Beast of Exmoor – Answers

August Letter – "The Beast of Exmoor"
(EXTRACT FROM THE STORY)

"Part of me felt I was being hunted... was I the prey?"

"... the creature leapt out of the water, and, with two bounds,

it was towering above my head"

To The Family

Dear Kids

I'm glad to hear you enjoyed the stories about the animals visiting my home in Haslemere.

Just, last week, I read a newspaper report, titled "British Big Beast bares its Teeth", and in part, it was about the Beast of Exmoor. When reading it, I remembered I'd long ago promised to write to you of my Exmoor adventure, involving an animal only a few people have ever seen in the wild. This animal secretly stalks and hunts in our countryside, especially on riverbanks and in our rivers.

We all kind of know what a Beast is, but you may be asking, "Where, and, what is Exmoor?" - And that would be a very, good question.

So, please forgive me if I take a little time to describe to you the beautiful landscape of north Devon and Somerset, where Exmoor straddles the two counties, in defiance of these man-made boundaries. I'll touch on some of the old legends that clothe this landscape, which is often misty and always mysterious. And I will also introduce you to some of the wild animals, big and small, that roam its magnificent moorland.

To the north, Exmoor's towering cliffs and Valley of the Rocks are home to feral, bearded goats and hardy ponies that stand guard over the Bristol Channel below. To the south, the moor gives way to a relaxed, rolling countryside of woods, fields and gentler moving rivers.

Exmoor's wild and craggy land is cloaked in mystery and ancient folklore, which are old stories and traditions. There are tales of witches that turned into hares, and pixies that could enter neither Heaven nor Hell so lived in caves and long-forgotten mines. There, they hid the bodies of disappeared local folk. It is said, The Devil himself scalped much of the landscape, before resting on an old bridge over the beautiful river Barle.

The high moorland sandstone has been sculpted by millions of years of powerful rain and strong winds. In places, tall cliffs overhang the valleys below as many rivers have cut deep ravines into the rock. Streams of fast-flowing water run excitedly from the highest, peaty ground into wooded dells as little waterfalls cascade down narrow gullies.

It was in one such valley that I had my magical and scary adventure.

Now, over the years there have been many stories about a large wild cat-like creature, the size of a panther, prowling this mystical moor, looking for unsuspecting fisherman to eat. People say the animal is as long from head to tail as the tallest man is high, and could leap a two-metre fence in a single bound. A killer like no other in our land.

With this in mind, I need to take you back 10 years when Auntie Bridget and I, along with a group of our neighbours, had rented a country house just south of Exmoor. I had been given permission to fish a hidden and rarely visited part of one of the rivers named after the moor, called the river Exe.

Well, the day of my adventure started early and in bright sunshine. The air was still, but cool, when I packed my fishing rod, rucksack and waterproof waders into the boot of the car. As I drove to the farm gate, I was met by a local farmer, who asked where I was fishing that day.

'One of the moorland landowners has kindly given me permission to fly-fish a stretch of the upper reaches of the river Exe, not too far from the village of Bridgetown,' I said.

'The river Exe you say?' the farmer questioned.

'Yes, I've got a map.'

'Upper reaches you say?'

'Err ... Yes, that's right. Is there a problem with that?'

The farmer breathed in, pursed his lips and leant on the gate as he looked up into the distance towards the Exe valley, which was now becoming draped in dark, slowly swirling clouds.

'See ...' the farmer continued ... 'There've been some mysterious goin's on up there, over the past few weeks ... Did you say you're fishing alone?'

'Well actually, yes I am. I understand nobody's been fishing there for a while.'

He looked back at me. 'There's a reason for that, see. Mysterious goin's on up there.'

'Oh, tell me more.'

'Not for me to say, but I hear sheep have been goin' missing in the night; half-eaten bodies found up the valley. Red deer, torn to pieces, I've heard ... Goin' alone you say?'

'Er, well, yes ...'

'Ah, guess I'd better be about my work,' said the farmer as he turned to close the gate behind me. 'Don't say I didn't warn you.'

'Warn me ... of what?'

'The Beast of Exmoor... That's what!' And with that, he was gone.

I had a lot to think about as I drove slowly up the valley towards the threatening black clouds and, eventually, I reached my destination. Dropping into a makeshift lay-by, next to a country track, I could see a small arched stone bridge, tucked away to my left, which matched the one marked on a tatty old map I'd been given.

After getting out of the car and pulling on my chest waders, I collected my fishing rod and rucksack from the back of the car and wandered up to the bridge.

Peering over, I could see the river far below, but couldn't make out any obvious way down to it. I checked the old map, again, and yes, I was in the correct place.

Looking more closely to my right, I noticed five or six large, flat stones protruding from the steep bank. They descended one after another from beside the top of the bridge to a small patch of gravelly ground next to the river. The stones were partially hidden by overhanging alder bushes, but maybe they once formed part of a long-forgotten set of steps. I was beginning to wonder if anybody had fished here for many years.

I glanced once more at the tattered old map and the dilapidated stone steps as I recalled the farmer's stories of the "Beast of Exmoor". *Was this really such a good idea to fish here?*

'Ah well, I'm here now,' I said encouragingly to myself as spots of rain and a gust of wind were accompanied by a single crack of thunder overhead.

It was then I heard the unfamiliar sound of a bird that I had only come across once before, at the Tower of London, but I recognised it instantly. It was the "Cawing" of a raven. I looked up and across the valley to the craggy hillside opposite. Through the swirling low clouds, I could just make out the distinctive shapes of two ravens.

Now at this point, I need to tell you a little more about the bygone beliefs of country folk. Ravens are thought to be mystical messengers, sometimes called "harbingers" that bring news of a future death or disaster. So, folklore was telling me that coming across two of these magnificent birds was a bad "omen" of danger ahead.

You might forgive me for having yet more doubts about whether this adventure was really a good idea: Rain and thunder, the ravens and finally the "Beast of Exmoor" on the prowl. What could possibly go wrong?

I thought for a moment and again peered over the bridge to the river, before climbing over a low fence to my right. Then, gripping onto a tangle of bushes for support, slowly, I side-stepped my way down the ancient stones.

As I jumped off the final slab, and onto the gravel of the tiny beach, it was as if I had stepped into a magical and forgotten world. From above, the light green canopy of trees dripped occasional glistening crystals of rainwater; whilst below, the air was filled with birdsong and the rich scent of wild garlic. Long, ruler-straight shafts of slanted sunlight seemed to switch on and off as they escaped down from the swaying leafy forest overhead.

Just a pebble's throw upstream, the river played hide-and-seek with itself as it danced with delight; dropping between; under and over small rocks and larger boulders. The water cheered and cried out as a thousand little waterfalls cascaded into the deep, quieter pool in front of me.

For a moment, time stood still as I looked and marvelled at the fairy-tale land of beauty that now surrounded me.

Never before had I felt so separated from the old world that I'd just left; a world beyond the umbrella of oak trees above. And never before had I felt as close to nature as I did, deep within the new world I'd now discovered.

Gone were the dark thoughts of the thunder; the harbingers of death and the Beast of Exmoor. But this was to change as the secrets of this wonderland were to be revealed.

I gathered together my rod, backpack and thoughts before scrambling over the rocks and rounding the first bend on the next stage of my adventure, upstream.

Over thousands of years, the power of the river had further cut this deep-sided gully into the main valley above. In places, the darting, twisting streams of water ran between overhanging cliffs that pinched the flow into faster running and free-falling torrents.

Each small waterfall created its own sparkling pool, into which I cast my fishing line with the hope of catching a wild and untamed trout. I moved from pool to pool, climbing over large boulders and ducking under the rocky outcrops, but I was never more than an arm's length away from the river.

At every pool, I stepped into the clear water that gently but repeatedly kissed the shoreline, and I ran my hands through the submerged gravel. The small pebbles and larger stones were laced with tiny wild creatures, which lived most of their life under the pool's surface. As a fisherman, I was familiar with most of them, and the imitation "flies" that I tie on the end of my fishing line are supposed to look like these bugs and beetles, but they never do.

All of these minute animals are called "invertebrates" because, unlike you and me, they don't have bones but instead have a shell-like skeleton. Most are as tiny as your fingernail and have glorious names like "Cased Cadis", "Gammarus" and my favourite, the "Baetis Nymph", which looks like a magical two-tailed fairy. She dances along the river bed and has her palace home under the submerged pebbles. And like "real" fairies and dryads, they always leave me spellbound with their delicate beauty.

The bugs and beetles were joined in their pebbly home by a funny-looking fish called a "Bullhead". They love clean, pure water and look different from any other river creature. I believe when God made all our fish, he stepped back to admire His work but unfortunately stood on the head of the Bullhead, flattening it into the shape we see today.

Whilst standing knee-deep in one of the pools, I heard in the distance the piercing call of our most beautiful river-dwelling bird. I looked behind me as the calling approached, and, as I did, a shining blur of brilliant blue and orange passed close by my head, just like a smear of bright paint on a canvas. I've often seen these shy little birds on my other fishing adventures, but it was extra special to be sharing this world of greens and greys with such a magnificently and brightly coloured *Kingfisher.*

'Wait for me my little friend,' I said in vain as he flew fast and low whilst following the river around the next bend and out of sight.

'Can't wait ... can't wait; fish to catch; family to feed - *There's trouble in the air,*' he seemed to reply in his high pitch call.

As I settled down on a large bolder, to eat my packed lunch, I looked up and realised the valley sides were so steep and rocky that there was no way of leaving this mysterious world, except by either retracing my steps or heading upstream and further into the unknown.

The birdsong had disappeared. Flowers and plant life had deserted the gully sides, and there was not a bee or beetle to be seen or heard. Who knows what may be around the next bend?

Suddenly, I felt trapped. Had I been tricked by this enchanted river to venture deeper and deeper into a much darker world; possibly one inhabited by demons, pixies, or worse ... *The Beast of Exmoor?*

I put away the remains of lunch and threw my rucksack over my shoulder, before dropping down into the water and moving around a particularly large boulder, the size and shape of a pouncing Dragon, which looked as if it was guarding the river's secrets. It was becoming difficult to scramble over the rocks beside the water, so now I spent more time wading up the river.

As the gully narrowed, the strength of the current grew stronger and stronger, pushing hard against my legs as if holding me back; trying to turn me around.

'Don't go on ... Don't go on!' the water urgently pleaded, as the river rushed noisily all around me.

As I rounded the tight bend to the right, exhausted with the constant pressure of the ever-deepening water, I was relieved to see the river ahead of me had relaxed into a gentle curve, as it widened and shallowed.

Leaving the agitated and chattering water behind me, I slowly continued to make my way up the centre of the flow. The world had become peaceful again, and a little lighter as the canopy of tree branches became thinner overhead. The birdsong returned, and once more I felt the calm I'd experienced a little earlier. But had I been given another warning; this time by the turbulent waters I had just left?

I could feel the crunching of clean riverbed gravel below my feet and stopped to cast another fly onto the soft, unbroken surface of the water, in front of me.

I was thinking just how tranquil my surroundings were when the kingfisher reappeared, flying directly towards me and accompanied by his familiar shrill call. Flashing passed, within arm's reach, he came to rest on an overhanging branch, just a few metres downstream. After a few seconds, the kingfisher tilted his head, as if either inspecting me or the water below, before diving, beak-first, into the crystal-clear stream. A few seconds later, he emerged with a tiny fish, sideways in his beak. He flew back to his perch and then hit the poor fish on the branch, before flipping it around and eating it head-first.

'Well you've done a lot better than I have at catching fish,' I said. 'Great trick, but I think I'd better stick with the fishing rod.'

I felt both comfort and concern at his return. I remembered ancient folklore of a calm time between two storms, when a female Kingfisher, called the Halcyon Bird, would briefly return to bring a short peace before a terrible event. Was the kingfisher's arrival linked to the warning given to me by the ravens, earlier today? Once again, I thought of the Exmoor Beast; prowling the countryside.

Fifty metres in front of me, I could see a wide waterfall, about the height of a man, over which the river cascaded. Making my way to the right, I clambered to the flat top of the giant slab. This rock had created the waterfall on its downstream side and a large dammed pond, the size of a small swimming pool, upstream.

I'd lost any idea of the time, but I must have been in the river for at least five hours. So I took off my backpack, sat on a dry part of the flat slab, and dangled my legs into the pool of calm, cool water. I lay back, and through the trees, I could see the broken clouds had revealed patches of Kingfisher-blue sky. All was well in my little, new

World; or so I thought.

I was still lying on my back and thinking of all the beauty I'd seen, heard and smelt when a distant, crashing noise behind me awakened my fearful attention.

A second, louder splash caused me to sit up straight and turn to look downstream. I slipped off the rock and into the pool, right up to my chest, and rested my crossed arms on the lip of the dam. I had a good view downstream from my vantage point but all I could see in the distance was a massive disturbance in the frothing water, just next to the right-hand bank. And then there was nothing; not a movement; not a sound. I held my breath.

I didn't know what to do - was it the Exmoor Beast? I couldn't run; I couldn't fight my way up the steep sides of the valley to escape; I was caught where I was. Maybe I'd be safe in the water, I thought. I could move to the centre of the pool, crouch down and hope not to be spotted. No, it was too deep.

Every little noise to my left and then to my right; caused me to snap around, believing it to be the creature. Was the Beast creeping behind me, getting ready to pounce on my back?

Part of me felt I was being hunted: ... was I the prey?

I began to fear the unknown.

Suddenly, and without any warning, the river erupted just below the waterfall, in front of where I was crouching in the pool. Within just a millisecond, the creature leapt out of the water, and, with two bounds, it was towering above my head, no more than two paces to my right.

I couldn't move; I couldn't breathe; I just froze, still three-quarters submerged in the cold water.

So there it was, the most magnificent, wild and elusive creature in our magical and mysterious land. A creature brought to the edge of extinction by hunting, decades before; a creature so rare that even now only a few people have ever seen it in the wild, and seldom in daylight.

Supported on four webbed feet, and at just over a metre long, she was covered from nose to tail in glistening, mottled-brown hair and displayed a lighter coloured tummy and chest. Strangely, her nose reminded me of Holly Dog's nose; moist and twitchy. But her flattish head, with small ears and short whiskers, concealed dagger-sharp canine teeth.

This was *not* "The Beast of Exmoor", but a young, female otter, sometimes called a sow, and she was almost within touching distance.

After resting for a minute, the otter moved slowly towards me. Clearly, she realised I was there because otters have fantastic senses of sight, smell and hearing. Now within a metre of me, she gave a dismissive sniff of her nose in my direction and returned along the rock to her original position as if to say;

'And who are you?' or 'What next then?'

Slowly, I turned around in the water, so my back was towards the dam head. Both of us were now looking into the deep pool.

'Well, my friend,' I whispered, 'how's *your* fishing been? I bet it was better than mine.'

I didn't get a reply; she just gave me a gentle nod as she lay down to relax on the rocky outcrop.

I tried again. 'Any chance you could give me a few tips on how to fish this river?' But, like all fisher-folk, she wasn't keen to offer much advice or give away her secrets; just a glance or two upstream.

Never in my life have I been, and felt, so close to such a wild creature as I was in that moment.

Cautiously, I lifted myself up with my elbows until I was sitting on the rock with my legs still dangling back in the water, just a couple of metres from my new friend. I tried not to make too much eye contact, hoping she would stay in place whilst I tried to reach my backpack. I don't know about you, but I can never find anything I want when I need it. And so it was with my little camera, which had hidden itself deep in the backpack.

I don't remember how long we both rested together; it felt like an hour, but it was probably less than ten minutes before she decided: 'Enough of this sitting around, I'll show you how to catch fish.'

With that, she slipped off the rock and into the pool, with hardly a splash. I was surprised that she didn't swim into the middle of the pool, in search of dinner, but returned to the margins of the river before diving and bobbing as she turned over the small pebbles ... she was hunting for small Bullheads or crayfish... not trout.

'Far too much like hard work,' she might have thought, and she was probably right.

Just at that point, I found my camera and managed to snap a couple of poor pictures of the foaming water made by the feeding otter.

I watched in awe as she continued her journey up the river, always keeping to the bankside. I remained at the pool and fished there for a while, reflecting and thinking about our meeting on this, the magical river Exe.

For several more hours, I fished the small pools upstream, without catching a single fish, until I reached another bridge. Finding more old stone steps, to the left this time, I staggered my way up to the lane above and back into my Old World. As I crossed the bridge, I looked back over the wall to the river below, for the last time.

A little distance down the lane, I was met by a local man and asked for directions on how I could quickly return to my parked car, by the other bridge, downstream, and, he obliged by pointing across the fields.

'It'll only take you fifteen minutes or so,' he said.

And as I looked at the map again, I saw the river had meandered backwards and forwards; turning this way and that. So as the "crow flies", or should I say, "the raven flies", I was only about a mile and a half from my car.

Interested in finding out a little more about the river, I quizzed the man further.

'Have you seen any otters on the river lately? I've just been fishing.'

'No, thank Goodness. Years ago we 'ad 'em 'ere. They 'ad all the fish; killed my chickens; ate my ducks ....I'd 'ave 'em all shot if they weren't protected by The Law ... Damned things! Haven't seen them here for decades ... But I thought I saw the Beast of Exmoor; justa couple of hours ago; coming up from the river ... Got my children inside just in time I reckon,' he teased. 'Strange things been goin on around 'ere ... sheep gone missing; red deer torn apart. Been fishing alone you say?'

'Yep ... *all* alone.'

He breathed in. 'Dangerous time around 'ere – did you see anything out of the ordinary down there then; maybe the Beast?'

'Nope; not me; haven't seen a thing ... all very quiet ... Didn't even catch a fish.'

'Waste of time then!' he exclaimed.

'Yes, I guess so ... *Just a waste of time*'.

***

I hope you've enjoyed this story as much as I have in recalling it for you. And, maybe one day we could plan and go together on an expedition to track down the *"Beast of Exmoor"*. Look at the next page for more interesting facts about otters.

In my next letter, we'll visit another, quite different river. And, I'll share with you some fun experiences I had as a boy and as a grown-up.

My best regards,
Uncle Steve

THE BEAST OF EXMOOR ACTIVITIES

Which ONE of these facts about otters is TRUE?

- Otters have four toes on each foot.
- Otters have been spotted recently in all UK counties except for the Isle of Wight and Anglesey.
- Otters have the densest (more follicles per square inch) fur of any other animal
- Otters have fewer teeth than adult humans.
- A male otter can have a territory of up to six miles of river.

The Beast of Exmoor

Try to find the scary words from Exmoor

Created with TheTeachersCorner.net Word Search Maker

```
Y  Q  H  W  L  P  K  Q  T  S  T  M  N  H  Z
S  Y  X  C  K  M  F  W  U  S  W  F  X  T  R
G  A  H  E  O  K  N  G  A  H  O  M  H  E  Y
Y  X  L  O  X  S  E  E  D  L  Y  Z  E  K  H
M  D  G  T  F  M  B  O  K  I  Y  D  W  G  J
N  G  A  S  K  U  O  L  N  L  D  R  K  O  I
T  H  M  W  K  C  O  O  O  E  H  P  M  Y  N
R  U  M  K  U  R  F  J  R  Z  Y  X  B  C  V
O  D  A  P  E  X  W  M  W  V  A  K  G  V  B
U  D  R  K  I  N  G  F  I  S  H  E  R  I  L
T  Y  U  X  O  K  C  D  A  E  H  L  L  U  B
V  H  S  T  J  B  F  T  H  M  Y  D  U  F  W
A  O  T  P  R  E  F  A  I  R  Y  T  A  L  E
Q  E  T  P  V  M  T  V  L  E  L  X  C  Q  G
R  E  R  M  R  J  Z  P  E  E  H  S  R  S  Y
```

BEAST	BULLHEAD	EXMOOR
FAIRYTALE	FOLKLORE	GAMMARUS
KINGFISHER	NYMPH	OTTER
REDDEER	SHEEP	TROUT

The answers can be found at the back of the book on page 242

The Beast of Exmoor Crossword

Can you fill in the crossword quiz below?

Created using the Crossword Maker on TheTeachersCorner.net

cross

2. Which fish did God accidently step on?
3. What feet did the creature have that sat next to me?
6. What brightly coloured bird flew along the river?
8. Which birds live in The Tower of London?

Down

1. What do we call the minute creatures that don't have bones?
4. Which mythical creatures couldn't enter Heaven or Hell?
5. Which animal sat on the damhead?
7. Which animal went missing in the night?

THE RIVER WEY

An underwater photo of a "not so hungry" Mr Chub

"Clearly, none of them was hungry and not at all interested in the silliness of a useless fisherman, like me."

A Fox in the grass on the banks of the Wey

"I saw a ball of golden-brown fur with two very pointed ears; two tightly closed eyes, and all wrapped in a magnificently fluffy duvet of a tail"

September Letter – "The River Wey"
(EXTRACT FROM THE STORY)

"Heads bobbed out; heads bobbed in, just like mini Jack-in-a-boxes, but, still no bodies"

To The Family

Dear Kids

I hope you may have had a chance to read my last letter about The Beast of Exmoor, but there has been so much excitement in your lives, with the start of the new school year, I shouldn't think you've had any time.

It's times like this when we feel the whole world is changing around us; new classes, new schools, new friends, and new experiences. But some things never change: the Sun rises and sets; nature's yearly cycle continues; mums and dads, wives and husbands, brothers and sisters can always be annoying.

Talking of parents being annoying, let me ask you a question: Have you ever been *ordered* to tidy your bedroom or *told* to throw away old, broken toys that hold special memories for you? Well, I have, and I bet this "tragedy" will happen to you in the future, if it hasn't already.

So, as this is to be one of my last letters to you as a family, I thought I would start by giving you two, "non-nature" related stories about toys that held special memories for me; one as a child and the other as a grownup. And, how the second story led me to remember some lovely little memories about my local river. See, nothing actually changes, and, as I've said before - *I never really grew up ... I just grew old.*

My Precious Rod – Part 1

When I was your age, my mummy would sometimes rummage through my old toys and collect together those she thought I wouldn't be playing with again. They were bagged-up and taken to "Jumble Sales" in our local Saltwood Village Hall, where they were sold, and the money was given to some "rotten old charity." *I never got a penny!* Nowadays, these toys would go to a Charity Shop.

It was heartbreaking to see my much-loved toy racing cars, battery-powered robots, and worst of all, wonky, one-eyed, one-armed teddy bears thrown into the sack. Often, I'd sulk in my room and concoct plans to rescue them, when my mummy wasn't looking.

Checking the coast was clear, I would sneak downstairs to the front door, where the imprisoned toys were being held captive in the sack, and retrieve my most precious possessions; a floppy chimpanzee, dressed as a sailor; a model car with flashing lights, and a small, brightly coloured box that played a tune when opened, were all liberated to rejoin the other toys; safe in my bedroom.

On one of these tragic "Jumble Sale" occasions, the sack had been whisked out of the house and locked in the boot of the car before a rescue mission had been possible. So I decided to undertake an expedition to the Village Hall in an effort to rescue a toy or two.

I went down to the Village Hall with my friend Zoe, who had experienced the same bereavement at the loss of her toys, to the "Horror Sale".

We crept in through the backdoor of the Hall, without paying the entrance fee, and started to look around the cavernous room with its shiny, dark wood floor, high vaulted ceiling and a raised, old-planked timber stage.

Long, wooden "fold-up" tables, piled high with tangles of old clothes bent uncomfortably next to stalls selling bedraggled garden plants and tatty, used books.

In the far corner, I could see my mummy busily serving cups of tea from behind a smartly decorated table, which displayed homemade cakes and scones. She had to be avoided at all cost, as she was bound to ask why we were there.

Passing a table that invited children to 'guess-the-name-of-the-doll', I spotted the 'Second-hand Toy' stall, and tugged Zoe's arm as I headed over to the 'toy prison'. At first glance, it was a treasure-trove of children's toys, but I knew each had a sad story to be told of being dragged away from the clutching arms of a screaming child, only hours earlier.

The bodies of moth-eaten clowns lay alongside colourful plastic trumpets, whilst broken, stringless puppets and scary-looking, winking dolls festooned the tabletop.

It was then I saw the horror to end all horrors, a quite unbelievable sight; one that leaves me feeling faint and dizzy to this very day. For at the back of the table, and I can hardly bring myself to say this, even after all these years, was my dearest possession: my very first fishing rod and reel, which embraced all my memories of Ghost Lake and the first fish I'd ever caught. How could my mother have committed such a crime of taking this most precious object? I think you'll agree; parents can be so cruel.

It was priced-up at two shillings and sixpence - that's twelve pence in

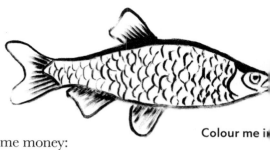

Colour me i◀

today's money. After a second or two, I managed to start breathing again, and urgently turned out my pockets in an unsuccessful attempt to find some money:

A short length of string; an old conker; a filthy   handkerchief; an empty and sticky sweet wrapper, and a button from a long-forgotten, pyjama top... That was the total contents of both pockets.

'Zoe, Zoe ... Zoeee! *Please* lend me *Half a Crown (twelve pennies)*,' I pleaded. 'I'll die if you don't.'

For a minute, she weighed up whether it was better I died rather than lend me her money.

Finally, she said, 'I've only got a shilling and ninepence, and I want to buy that little teddy bear, over there. She's so sweet.'

'WHAT! A scummy old bear or my fishing rod ... life's so unfair,' I thought to myself.

'Okay, Okay. Give me the money, and I'll see what I can do to get both,' I replied quickly.

With the money in my hand, I approached the stallholder.

'Err, how much for the bear and the old fishing rod?' I asked politely, but confidently.

Looking at the price labels, the little old lady behind the table added the two values together.

'Well, it looks like Three Shillings (fifteen pennies).'

'I've got a shilling and ninepence, a hanky and a button. Will that do?'

I offered them up in my outstretched hand. I wasn't about to give up the string or the conker without further negotiation.

'I'm not sure the reel works; it looks pretty old,' she said

'NOT SURE IT WORKS? ... Silly old Bat ... of course, it works! I caught my first Roach with that Rod and Reel,' I muttered, under my breath.

Well, the deal was done, less the button and hanky, both of which were then shoved back into their respective pockets.

With our two prizes in hand, Zoe and I crept back out of the hall, without been seem by my traitorous mother, and we skipped home in triumph.

I'm not sure if I ever repaid Zoe, but I still remember the great feeling of being reunited with my "precious fishing rod".

My Precious Rods – Part 2 (Fifty-Five Years Later)

Now, there's an old saying – "What goes around, comes around", and, just the other day, Auntie Bridget discovered some of my old fishing equipment in our loft, which I'd been hiding out of her way for many years.

Much of it was bought at auctions, and the rest from fishing tackle shops, which to me are like visiting the most exciting treasure-caves of discovery in the world. Every rod; every float; every reel for sale offers the promise of catching more fish; bigger fish; better fish ... And over the years, I've just had to buy them all.

'Well, you're just going to have to get rid of all this clutter ... every last bit of it,' Auntie Bridget insisted as she started to clear the loft-space. 'I bet you don't even know what's up here .... And when did you last use this?' she said, pointing towards an old fishing bag, which had been home to a family of mice over several winters.

'Oh my Goodness, it's full of mouse droppings,' she screeched, after a closer inspection. 'It's absolutely disgusting!' Auntie B stared at me as if I'd been personally responsible for the offending poo.

'It wasn't me "Miss', honest ... it was them mice what did it.'

I started my defence of the offending bag:

'Surely, with a quick clean-up and a few stitches here and there, it could be repai....,' but I was abruptly interrupted.

'OUT!' came the order from Auntie B.

Forty-five minutes later, the loft was clear of all my precious fishing gear; one half of which was spread out on the back lawn, and the other was thrown into the dustbin by Auntie Bridget.

Old rods and backpacks brought back happy memories of fishing on my favourite river, the river Wey, which winds its course near my house, on a one-way journey to join the river Thames, close to London.

Every item I handled, got me thinking about adventures I've had on this little river, and I thought you may be interested to hear about one or two of them.

Memories of the river Wey

At the bottom end of the river Wey, where it meets the Thames, the water trudges to its destination. Shackled by waterway navigations, it's like a weary, old carthorse at the end of a long day. But nearer to its start, or *source*, the river can be quite lively and excitable, more similar to a frisky foal than a carthorse. It is this part of the river where I like to walk, fish and dream.

So here is a small selection of very, short stories about this lovely, little, meandering river.

There's a "Hippopotamus" in the river!

I love walking along the riverbank, with just a fishing rod in one hand and a small 'landing net' in the other. Sometimes, I don't fish, I just look, listen and breathe in deeply, to enjoy the rich scent of the water and riverside plants.

Like an Amazon explorer, I have to fight my way through the tall, thick foliage of reedmace, comfrey, and stinging nettles to get to the water's edge.

On a hot July day last year, I had, unsuccessfully, tried to catch a fish called a *chub*. Clearly, none of them was hungry and not at all interested in the silliness of a useless fisherman, like me.

I was determined to find the best position to release my float and line into the moving current of the river; and also to hide from Mr and Mrs Chub. So, I decided to crawl on all fours through the undergrowth to the riverside. From experience, I knew it was often difficult to see where the riverbank stops and the river-water starts, as the plants have a liking for hanging over the bank to watch the river go bubbling by. I got into what I believed was a great position, with the water revealed just in front of me. I flicked out the line from my rod tip and watched the float jauntily bob its way downstream. Now, I couldn't see much of its journey, due to the reeds. To get a better view of Mr Float's progress, I leant forwards, supporting my weight by placing my left hand on the "riverbank" in front of me, whilst holding the rod in my right. Unfortunately, it wasn't the riverbank that I'd leaned on; it was some flimsy foliage, bending over the river. As the plants gave way under my massive bulk, I slowly slid forwards, head-first into the river, like a very, clumsy, fat Hippopotamus reluctantly entering a cold pool of water at a Zoo ... Splash! If there had been a fish or two nearby, my dramatic entrance would have sent them scattering in fear ... or laughter.

Luckily for me, the river was just chest deep, but, even so, when I finally floated to the surface, choking and spluttering, I was relieved to be able to take a breath of air.

With wet riverweed still draped over my head like a scarf, I floundered my way to the bankside, threw my rod into the reeds and struggled out of the water where I'd entered it.

I was soaked from head to toe, and my wader-boots were full of mucky, brown water. I took them off and emptied their contents back into the river. Fortunately, I had some spare clothes in my backpack, along with an unopened packet of Jammy-Dodger biscuits, all of which had stayed nice and dry on the riverbank. I peeled off my wet garments and slipped on a pair of shorts and a T-shirt, whilst devouring a couple of the biscuits.

There was little or no chance of catching a fish, at least for an hour or two, so I decided to partake in my second-favourite pastime after fishing, and that's having an afternoon nap.

I put my rod to one side and spread out my waders and fishing jacket to dry in the sun. With both hands behind my head, I made myself snug and comfortable, lying flat-out amongst the tall reeds, as if I was in a giant, cosy nest.

As I was nodding off to the relaxing sound of the chattering river, I heard a rustling sound coming from the reeds nearby. Very often coots, moorhens and mallard ducks will rest-up in these jungle river margins of plants and bushes, so I thought nothing of it and glided off to the world of dreams, where I always catch the biggest fish.

A few minutes later, I awoke with a bit of a jolt. There it was again, but this time the sound of the disturbance seemed a little closer. I sat up and listened, but all was silent again.

Intrigued, I decided to take a sneaky peek. Kneeling, I slowly parted the reeds with both hands, as if swimming breaststroke in a pool of plants.

It didn't take long for me to find out exactly what had been making the noise. As there, in a clearing amongst the reeds, much the same as my "nest", I saw a ball of golden-brown fur with two very pointed ears; two tightly closed eyes, and all wrapped in a magnificently fluffy duvet of a tail.

It was a young fox, taking advantage of the warmth of this beautiful sunny day by having a doze on the riverbank, just like me; one of us nice and dry and the other still rather damp.

Quietly, I reversed back to my patch of heaven and promptly fell asleep.

I don't know how long I slept, but when I woke up, my clothes were dryish and the fox was gone ... Along with *my* Jammy Dodger biscuits; packet and all.

'Ah well, *"share and share alike,"*' I thought to myself as I pulled-on the damp waders, collected my rod and backpack, before leaving my "nest" to continue fishing.

***

The Giant Oaf

Over the years, I've helped, a little, to make our rivers better places for wildlife. On one occasion, I was with Jim, from the Surrey Wildlife Trust, gathering small tree-trunks and larger branches for a "restoration" project, near to a part of the river Wey that I looked after.

Several of our bankside "crack" willow trees had lost thick branches in the winter gales. Some had fallen on the riverbank and others into the river, all of which we left alone to improve the surroundings for wildlife to live in. But some tree boughs had dropped into the fields next to the river, where the cattle graze, and they didn't really need the wood.

After Jim and I had cut and loaded the last of three trailers of timber, Jim drove off with the wood securely tied down, whilst I decided to walk along the river.

The day sat uncomfortably heavy and quiet, with a little cloud and the threat of drizzle in the air. At times like this, there is always wildlife to see if you look for it.

Bees were busily buzzing from flower to flower as spooked birds lifted from the reeds and sped away; flying low over the open fields. A massive heron laboriously took flight from the shallows and slowly followed after the other departing birds. Stick-like, blue damselflies danced over the river, and "Whirligig" beetles spun around and around on the water's surface, like dodgem cars at a fairground.

This was a world I'd been a part of for many years, and I knew every twist and turn of the river; each deep and shallow pool, and, every tree and bush on the bankside.

One of my favourite stop-off points was a small grassy mound that sat between, and under, two overhanging, stunted willow trees. Previously, a family or two of rabbits had lived here, in burrows dug out of the sandy soil. They'd long gone, due to the risk of their home getting flooded in winter storms, but the burrows remained and often provided a safe, summer residence for beetles, shrews and even the odd grass snake; all looking for overnight accommodation.

As I made myself comfortable on the patch of scrubby grass, I noticed the sand around two of the burrows, either side of my feet, had been recently disturbed, and it was a little damper than the surrounding soil. This can often be a sign that an animal has been visiting. I sat very still and kept my feet together, between the burrows, which opened away from me and towards the river.

It wasn't long before I saw a tiny, light brown, furry face peeking out from one of the burrows. With a white chin and throat, stubby nose, rounded ears, twitching whiskers and coal-black pinpricks for eyes, he or she was suddenly aware of me being there and quickly darted back down the hole. A minute later, a second face popped out of the other burrow, and, as before, it took one look at my huge feet and disappeared.

Now, I had a pretty good idea just what type, or species, of animal I'd just seen, but I couldn't be certain. And, was it the same, single creature, just running underground between the two holes? I thought my new acquaintance was unlikely to come back out, now it knew I was here.

I was wrong, because a few minutes later, not one, not two, but four faces appeared from the same burrow. Clearly, word had got around that there was a strange, "B*ig Oaf of a thing*," sitting outside their two front doors.

Heads bobbed out; heads bobbed in, just like mini Jack-in-a-boxes, but still no bodies, and, more importantly, no tails.

Now that was important to me because I needed to see the very tip of their tails before identifying exactly what I was looking at, or should I say, *what was looking at me*.

The family name for this group of animals is "mustelid", but it was still a little while until one of the little fellows decided to be brave and venture out of the burrow to greet me. He, or she, was about 15 cm long and had white, flat, furry paws. The creature's body was long, thin and very sleek. Keeping low to the ground it crawled towards me in a "stop-start" manner. Only then, I saw the much darker brown colour tip of its tail, and I knew I was being welcomed by a family of stoats, rather than weasels. These were youngsters, as adults have a much blacker tail-tip and would have been a little larger. Grown-up weasels have a white-tipped tail, but their young have short, plain chestnut brown tails.

Soon they were popping out from both burrows, running from one to another around my feet and lower legs. One very bold little fellow even scurried backwards and forwards over my boots. I guess my arrival had interrupted playtime - but obviously not for long.

It was impossible to count how many there were as they rolled about together in play; falling down one rabbit hole, and reappearing from another. I estimated there could have been at least six of them, if not more. Life for the young stoats seemed like endless play, and they used me as a new ride in their own private fairground.

A high-pitched squeak caught their attention as mother stoat appeared from the reeds. She had stopped in her tracks when she saw me and the frolicking kits playing together. A hiss from her was followed by a slightly louder "bark", which sent all the kits rushing, as one, down their closest burrow. Only mother stoats raise the young. And normally the family would simply ignore the presence of a nearby person. But, clearly, I was far too close for her comfort on this occasion. I was pretty sure that if I hadn't been there, the youngsters would have run over to her in search of lunch.

I lifted my knees and withdrew my feet from between the burrows as mum skipped over and darted down the nearest hole. She didn't have their food, but sometimes, if her prey is too large, she will take her "caravan of kits" on a picnic, away from the burrow. They'll often follow her, looking like a string of little chipolata sausages, bouncing their way through the reeds or long grass.

I waited for a couple of minutes, but nobody decided to reappear, so I got to my feet and crept away. Having been disturbed, she would most likely move her large family to different "rented" accommodation, along the riverbank. It was also time for me to move on, and rejoin Jim.

A surprise swimmer in the river

I've said before, I love getting into rivers to fish or simply to have a different view of the world and my surroundings.

Likewise, if you were to lie on your bedroom floor and look around, you'll see just how different The World looks from the ground, compared to when you're standing in the middle of the room. You might discover some things under your bed that you didn't know were there; or find a spider, hidden under a chair. It's just the same when standing in a river. The bankside often towers over the water, and I can peer into dark places where the current has eaten away under the bank, exposing little cave-like hidden worlds for fish, ducks and other river creatures to live. And, just the other day, I found a grass snake under an overgrown riverbank with a strangely shaped fish called a bullhead, the size of your thumb, in its mouth. Amazing! The overhanging gaggles of plants have wonderful names like Bulrush and Great Hairy Willowherb. But one of my favourites is the voluptuous Comfrey, which I like to call "Mrs Clarissa Comfrey" because of her "bonnet shaped", pink or white flowers, and her designer-coat of richly textured, thick green leaves. She has a hairy stalk, which reminds me of my old auntie's hairy chin, and she always looks so surprised to see an "outsider" in "her" river. Mrs Comfrey and her friends, shake their heads in disapproval as I jostle past, waste-deep in the water.

'How *rude*! Who invited him into our world?' they whisper amongst themselves.

'Sorry ... sorry ... sorry,' I apologise, and I respectfully bow my head to each of them in turn.

'*I should think so too,*' Mrs Comfrey retorts, whilst readjusting her ladylike, leafy lingerie. And young stinging nettles hide behind her skirt, ready to pounce on the careless fisherman who dares to touch her.

Moorhens, a type of bird, stay still in their bankside hideouts, until, without warning and in a total panic, they scamper across the water's surface to reach the safety of the downstream reed beds. With a flurry of feathers and wings, they excitedly squawk out loud:

'It's the end of the world, I tell you ... the End!'... 'Run for your life!' they instruct.

Thinking about it, I can't remember ever actually seeing a moorhen fly. Maybe they are like mini flightless ostriches, or just suffer from a fear of heights.

Wild animals, like foxes and badgers, seem less frightened of humans when they see us in the water, and go about their business with little regard to our presence. And, even the fish are less wary of the big, green wader-boots standing mid-stream. I've often had trout or perch swim between my legs as I moved upstream. Little minnows and baby fish, called fry, will follow my every step, looking for tiny bits of food, disturbed from the riverbed by my huge boots.

Now, before I tell you about the strangest encounter I have ever had, whilst river wading, I must give you the sternest of warnings. It can be very dangerous going into a river, stream or pond, and you must never wade in rivers without an adult being with you, and never without wearing the right equipment, including a lifejacket. If the water is flowing fast, you should not enter the water, with or without an adult. It's all too easy to stumble on rocks or stones and catch your feet between, or under, hidden obstacles. Even in shallow, slower flowing water, a stream can push you under, especially if your foot gets stuck.

All that said, when in a river, I feel closer to wild nature than anywhere else on earth, and this brings me, in a somewhat roundabout way, to my story.

'Thank goodness,' I hear you say.

Well, after finishing an afternoon of river conservation work, with my friend Andy from the Wild Trout Trust, I grabbed my rod and fishing bag from the boot of my car and walked along the riverbank. I passed a long, straight stretch of the river that I knew was both deep and hazardous until I reached the first of several bends in the watercourse. This part of the river Wey was shallower and had little steps cut into the bank, to allow easier access.

I waded from bend to bend, fishing as I went. It was early autumn, and the trees were turning from the tired green of late summer to golden brown, and their dry leaves gently rattled in the light breeze. The thinning branches of the bankside weeping willows swayed as they caressed the surface of the river, like hair hanging over the shoulders of a river-mermaid.

The sun was setting far upstream to the west as a bird, called a snipe, flew up from the reeds beside me before it zigzagged in low flight down the river. I heard the sound of a fox barking from a distant wood, and decided it was time to wade back to the steps where I'd entered the water.

The river gently slapped the back of my waders as I reached the final bend, but before I clambered out of the river, I peered down the long stretch of deep water I'd walked along side earlier. Then, in the distant darkening twilight, I saw a splash as something seemed to be entering the river. Intrigued, I moved to calm water near the bank, where the riverbed was firm, flat and not so deep. To my amazement, whatever had entered the water was now moving slowly up the centre of the river towards me, and against the flow. As the river was at least two metres deep, I knew whatever was in the water had to be swimming rather than wading. Maybe it was somebody in a canoe. No, it just didn't look quite right for a boat as the object got closer.

It was only when the mystery swimmer came within fifty metres, I realised what I was witnessing. Heading my way was a handsome, male roe deer, called a roebuck, and he was adorned with a pair of magnificent antlers, which he would use to fight other stags in the "rutting", or "breeding" season. I can only guess he was swimming up the river to find somewhere to climb up the right bank, on his journey to find a group of female roe deer, called does.

I was sure he could see me, but still, he kept coming until he finally got his footing on the riverbed as it shallowed; no more than a couple metres from where I was standing, waist-deep in the river. I could now see every detail of his sleek, black muzzle; golden brown, coarse body hair and gnarled antlers.

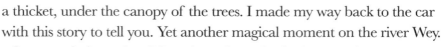

   With only a glance in my direction, he powerfully but gracefully moved up the bank and through the undergrowth to the open fields. Then he made his way over to the woods, as if being called by the fox, which had barked earlier. His elegance was breathtakingly beautiful.

   I scrambled out of the river, somewhat less gracefully than the deer, as he disappeared into a thicket, under the canopy of the trees. I made my way back to the car with this story to tell you. Yet another magical moment on the river Wey.

   It was only later that I found out from Andy that roe deer can not only swim but swim well.

   All rivers and streams are important to so many of our animals and plants as they connect different parts of our countryside, like a wild superhighway. I'm sure there are some little streams near to you. So maybe one day we could walk together along part of your river or stream. What do you think?

***

Well, I hope you have enjoyed my little trips down both the river Wey and my memory lane.

Finest Regards,
Uncle Steve

PS Auntie B has just found a tiny toad in one of her flower beds, but it wandered away before she could get a photo.

RIVER WEY ACTIVITIES

Which ONE of the following statement is FALSE?

• Stoats are related to badgers
• Stoats a can have white coats in winter
• Stoats normally have two litters (families of babies) per year; one in early spring and the other in mid-autumn or just before winter.
• Stoats bounce up and down whenever they run about. However, weasels don't bounce when they run.
• Stoats are up to three times bigger than weasels.

Creatures of the River Wey

Can you unscramble the letters below to reveal the animals in the stories

Created on TheTeachersCorner.net Scramble Maker

1. spaoopupmhit	Normally lives in Africa
2. bcuh	The name of a fish that lives in rivers
3. coto	A kind of water loving bird
4. onoerhm	Another bird that likes water
5. lebsete	This animal featured in the Robin Story
6. imesdfalsel	Like a dragonfly
7. arbbit	Lives in a warren
8. atost	Not a weasel
9. boekcur	A type of male deer

oat   hippopotamus   coot   roebuck   beetles   chub   rabbit   damselflies   moorhen

The answers can be found at the back of the book on page 244

A LITTLE, EARLY CHRISTMAS TREAT

"When our backs were turned, Holly Dog took her chance
and grabbed the huge lump of ham from the plate"

November Letter:
"A Little, Early Christmas Treat"
(EXTRACT FROM THE STORY)

"Get under the bed, and save our dinner

or I'll never speak to you again"

To The Family
Date: Late November

Dear Kids

Today is Friday, Auntie B has just nipped out to buy Holly Dog some of her favourite treats, and I'm sitting at my desk, looking out of the window on a drizzly day, and thinking to myself:
  'Who can I write a little letter to this afternoon?'
  Well, I must have been thinking aloud as I'm sure I heard Holly Dog say;
  'The Kids!'
  Or maybe, she just had a little bit of burpy wind; a trait that both Holly Dog and I share when we've drunk a glass of fizzy lemonade too quickly.
  'What a fine idea,' I replied as she lay, on "her" little sofa next to me.
  The next question I had for Holly Dog was:
  'And, what story should I write; maybe something a little different?'
  'Now, I could tell them about the young, and very well-dressed

magpie, who's just moved into the garden,' I suggested to Holly Dog.

"Master Magpie" is very tame, and Auntie Bridget has taken rather a fancy to him. He is slim, good looking, extremely "dapper" and full of life ... everything I'm not! He gives Auntie B lots of attention when she's in the garden, sunbathing. Often he hops right under her sun-lounger, in pursuit of a fly or beetle. I hear them chatting away to each other, about the latest Milan fashions, and which suntan oil offers the best UV protection.

'No, I refuse to tell you anything about him, as I'm just a little bit jealous of the attention he's getting from Auntie B,' I say to myself.

I think again, and then, consult Holly Dog;

'On the other hand, I could tell the kids about the family of blue tits that are visiting Auntie B's coconut feeder.' I place my forefinger across my closed lips; and consider.

'Hmm.'

The feeder hangs outside our bedroom window, and I've no idea where the family suddenly appeared from. But, just like a travelling circus troupe, they have set-up camp in our cherry tree, and now move between tree and coconut as if on a trapeze; occasionally, one or two at a time, but often, all six of them together. Once on the feeder, they flip about from the string to the top of the coconut; then, to the bottom; then, to the side; and then, back up to the top again. All of this, whilst the feeder swings from left to right; and around and around; it makes me dizzy to watch them. I've counted up to five blue tits on the coconut at any one time. When the sixth arrives, he knocks the smallest sibling off the coconut as if to say ... "And for my next trick!" Auntie B always claps her approval for their circus act, and shouts out; "Bravo; More, More!"

'But No, I'm not going to tell you about the blue tits, as they are too extrovert, and already get enough attention from Auntie Bridget,' I conclude.

'So what little story can I offer the children? .... Hmmm.' Holly Dog sighs.

'What's that you say, Holly Dog? ... Tell everybody about you, and the joint of Ham! That's a good idea,' I say, in congratulation.

She looks very proud of herself when really, she should feel guilty.

Okay, so, here goes.

Anyone for another slice of Christmas turkey?

A question for you: What do Holly Dog, your Grandma's oldest chair, and I have in common with each other? .... Got it yet? .... Well, nowadays, all three of us "creak" a lot when we move ... but it wasn't always like that, and Holly Dog was a very fast runner, as you'll find out later in the story.

***

One Christmas Day, twelve years ago, Auntie B and I had the whole family over for Christmas lunch. In total, there were fourteen of us, plus the ever-attentive Holly Dog. Candles were lit, carols were sung, and presents were opened. Lots of lemonade was drunk, so, burps and pops were aplenty as the fire crackled in the open hearth, with the addition of each log.

As always, Holly Dog sat on my left, waiting for the odd food-scrap or two, whilst I sat at the head of the table and carved the turkey and joint of ham. The conversations got louder, and the jokes a little ruder as Christmas crackers were pulled and heads were adorned with paper crowns.

Now, all good Christmas dinners come to an end when everybody has had too much to eat, and, as we left the table to start clearing up, I made the critical error of, temporarily, putting the remains of the ham on our "low level" sideboard. Meanwhile, I took the leftover turkey to the kitchen.

We had rather a lot of uneaten ham, for which I fully blame Auntie B because when ordering the meat, she did so in kilograms rather than pounds. This meant the ham was as big as a car tyre and twice as thick. What remained could have fed a small country for a week. But instead of donating the ham to Luxembourg, it was to be split amongst family members, for them to take home and have it cold over the next six months.

Things didn't quite go to plan.

When our backs were turned, Holly Dog took her chance and grabbed the huge lump of ham from the plate. This went unnoticed for no more than ten seconds, but it was just enough time for Holly Dog to make her escape from the dining room.

The shout went out from my daughter, Claire:

'Holly's got the Ham!'

With that, plates were dropped; waste Christmas wrapping paper was scattered across the floor, and elderly relatives needed medical attention.

Clearly, the ham was far too big for her to eat, as it was still the size of a half-deflated football. But as she valiantly tried to gobble and run at the same time, massive chunks of ham were being scattered in her wake; each piece of which tripped up the pack of chasing relatives ... the meat was everywhere.

Through the hallway she went; then, into the snooker room; then, under the table; then, up the stairs before finally disappearing beneath a double bed, where she came to rest under the watching eyes of the arriving family.

As ever, Auntie B put the blame for this disaster squarely onto my shoulders, and instructed me to: 'Get under the bed, right now, and save our dinner or I'll never speak to you again.'

'Hmmm, a tempting alternative,' I thought.

Anyway, down I went, under the bed, to join the growling dog, and I started negotiations for the return of what remained of the ham. But to no avail; she wasn't in a sharing mood.

I crawled back out from under the bed, empty-handed, but with a secret, cunning plan to feed the family over the coming week or two.

Now, I'm not proud of what I did next, and this is between you and me. You're sworn to secrecy.

As the entire family continued to peer under the bed at the spectacle of Holly Dog, eating their future dinners, I crept downstairs, collected all the fragments of ham that had been scattered by the fleeing Holly Dog, and hid them in the bottom of the fridge.

When the dust had settled, and everybody returned downstairs, except for the disgraced Holly Dog, the family discussion turned to the menu arrangements for the following week, and more exactly, what were we going to have to eat?

However, Auntie B had her own, very clear plan as to what was going to happen. The morning after Boxing Day, I was to be sent out, with my own money, and buy another piece of ham. Then, once back home, I was to cook it, whilst the rest of the family went out for a day to a local fair.

Well, two days passed, and they all had a fun day at the fair before coming home to a lovely, ham salad dinner. But, I didn't buy another ham from the butcher. And, I didn't spend the afternoon cooking the ham that I hadn't bought from the butcher ... because, by chance, I happened to find some delicious, slightly chewed ham pieces at the bottom of the fridge.

To this day only you, Holly Dog and I know exactly where that delicious cold ham came from; and the journey it took to get onto their plates. It's our secret. So, if you happen to "meat"-up with Auntie B, remember: "Mum's the Word".

I hope you enjoyed this, different, little story as we approach your Christmas holiday. Watch out, if you, too, have a dog.

Now, I haven't got an activity that involves chasing dogs around the house, so, thinking forward to summer evenings, I have written a note about how you can have your own adventure at night, hunting moths. It's easy because the moths come to you ... have a go at my 'Moth Trapping Guide' activity page.

My very, best regards,
Uncle Steve

NIGHT TIME FUN ACTIVITIES

Moth Trapping or "Mothing*" on summer evenings. (* - Just for clarity, "moth-ing" is my own, made-up word for moth watching)

There are well over 2000 different moth species in our country alone, compared with just 57 species of resident butterfly. Some moths migrate all the way from Africa. Very often moths are brightly coloured and are very important pollinators for many of our plants. Some flowers give off more scent at night than in the daytime, especially to attract moths. So, here are three ways of seeing moths and each method brings them to you at dusk on a summer's night ... simple!

"MOTHING METHODS – 1,2,3."

1. "Mothing 1" - Just open your curtains after dark and leave the indoor light on ... within an hour, you should have different moths on the outside of your window, clambering to get in. This is a great way of looking at moths from underneath, through the glass. Then go outside to see them from above. They will look very different on both sides.

2. "Mothing 2" - Hang a white, thin towel or white sheet over a washing line or long piece of string in your garden in a dark place (or balcony). Then, leave a torch or light shining up at the cloth and wait or go back inside for as long as you can before returning. Hopefully, the moths will be ready and waiting for you to look at, hanging on the cloth.

3. "Mothing 3" - Some moths are attracted more by scent. So, do exactly as above but this time wet strips of strong paper towel with concentrated fruit juice (or fizzy drink). Then hang these strips next to or over the white sheet or towel. If you don't have any juice, just take

50ml of water, boil it and add as much sugar as will dissolve. I've heard some people also add a little red wine at this stage. Let it cool and then use this sugar water to wet the paper towel strips. You can always substitute the paper towel for strips of cloth, if it gets too soggy.

If you then take photos of each type of moth you see, you can go online to identify them. You may also count how many of each species you have and then repeat the "experiment" each week and see how the different moths appear throughout the summer and beyond. Keep a record. Keep a lookout for the Privet Hawk Moth, Tiger Moth, the strange shaped Poplar Hawk Moth (pink and brown), and even the Elephant Hawk Moth.

It's important not to touch the moths and avoid moth trapping with a light every night.

My thanks to "UK Moths" and Butterfly Conservation.

NOVEMBER LETTER - "A LITTLE, EARLY CHRISTMAS TREAT"

Use this page to draw a picture of a moth you have seen or imagine.

THE GARDEN FAMILY FAREWELL

Beatrice Blackbird

"'Did you hear what she just said to me?' smiled Auntie Bridget"

December Letter:
"The Garden Family Farewell"

(EXTRACT FROM THE STORY)

"You're crazy going up there at this time of night."

"... my head-torch revealed the stripy bear-like creature, rummaging deep in the grass cuttings."

To The Family

Dear Kids

Well, as this year draws to a close, the excitement of Christmas opens its arms and welcomes us once more. And now, it's time for me to write my last letter to you.

So much has happened in all our lives over the past twelve months, and the riches offered to us by nature have never been clearer. I guess that due to the virus, each of us has had a little more time to look at life in our local parks, gardens and even in our homes.

Through these accidental letters, we've been able to journey in time and across our lovely land. We've met many animals and some plants that make our local world so wonderful and exciting. We've shared sorrow, fear, happiness, fun, friendship and discovery. So, I thought this letter would be a great opportunity, for me, to let you know how the members of our animal family have finished up their year.

This evening, I was all set for another fishing adventure, to seek out Esox Lucius, but the weather is wet and the rivers are running dangerously high. But as winter approaches you can be sure I'll soon again be visiting the riverbanks.

Colour me in!

In fact, it's been so wet, the worms are peering out from the lawn and asking, "Who left the tap running? We're drenched down here."

A pair of colourful Jays and a single squirrel, are busily burying acorns, deep-down under the grass in "Wormland". They're hiding this food-store of acorns and sweet chestnuts in readiness for a hard, cold winter.

In the past week, the wind-shaken leaves of our grapevine have gone from a patchwork of green to amber and then red, just like a rather confused, slowly changing traffic light.

'Go ... no wait ... Stop! ... Yes Go ... No Stop!' ... it dithers as the autumn breeze bustles past.

Recently, this grapevine has been attracting lots of attention. Female wasps continue to hunt for spiders and visit the ripening grapes on my vine for a drink of juice, and they have company. Holly Dog secretly sneaks off to see if any grapes have dropped to the ground, which worries me because grapes are not good for dogs. Holly Dog and the wasps aren't the only garden resident that have been caught stealing MY grapes.

Beatrice Blackbird and the Flying Beasts

The thieving of my grapes leads me nicely into telling you about Beatrice Blackbird, and in particular what happened yesterday afternoon.

Beatrice Blackbird, she that prefers showers to baths, is now in her teenage time. Her plumage is neither that of a youngster nor an adult, and with her speckled chest and slightly dishevelled feathers, I think she's looking a little "punkish". I reckon she has taken clothing tips from our young thrushes as she looks more like them than a blackbird.

Beatrice has a big attitude problem at the moment and won't be told what to do; either by her own mother or Auntie Bridget. Allow me to give you this example:

Now, the old grapevine creeps up the side of our house, right next to where our little fox used to sleep all those years ago, and I'm famous for making undrinkable wine from its fruit. Well, at this time of the year the grapes are about two weeks away from being ready to pick, but our blackbird family, along with the wasps, love to eat them just as they are.

So, yesterday afternoon, Auntie Bridget went out to shoo-off the family from the vine. Mother blackbird left as ordered and called out for Beatrice to follow. However, Beatrice had absolutely no intention of doing what her mum said as; "Beatrice knows best", and she remained deep amongst the vine leaves.

At this point, Auntie B got rather cross with her,

and a heated conversation followed:

'Young lady, I've told you to get out of the vine and go straight to your bedroom,' ordered Auntie Bridget, whilst pointing back at the laurel bush.

Beatrice just turned her back and simply refused to move.

Auntie B wasn't about to put up with this kind of bad behaviour.

'Don't look away from me when I'm telling you off,' exclaimed Auntie B. 'I'm old enough to be your Great, Great' ... thirty "Greats" later ... 'Great Grandmother. You will do what I say.'

With that, Auntie B reached into the vine to give Beatrice a poke with her broom handle.

In a fit of rage, Beatrice turned to Auntie B, used bad language that I can't repeat in this letter, and eventually scurried out of the vine "cafe".

'Did you hear what she just said to me?' smiled Auntie Bridget

I laughed. 'She's a Fowl mouthed teenager, wouldn't you say?'

Auntie B groaned at my poor attempt at humour and, promptly disappeared inside. 30 minutes later, she re-emerged with an almost life-sized scarecrow, or should that be scare-blackbird, made from newspaper, stuffed into some of my old clothes.

'How dare Beatrice have that attitude with me,' Auntie B jested as she sat the manikin on one of our garden seats. 'I thought we were bath-time buddies.'

As Auntie Bridget and I sat back on our garden chairs to admire her handy work, Beatrice reappeared and looked our way before she flew over and landed on the scarecrow's hat. Neither of us could quite believe the cheek of it. But then Beatrice, without notice, urgently scampered back to the refuge of the laurel hedge.

'Wow ... why was she in such a hurry?' I said.

Before Auntie Bridget could reply, two very large and familiar dark shadows crossed the lawn next to us. Immediately, we both looked up to see the pair of adult ravens passing slowly overhead, no higher than the roof of our house. Except for the odd heron and wandering osprey, these ravens are the biggest birds to visit our neighbourhood, and, having seen us, they circled once as if checking out the garden before heading towards the setting sun in the west. Stunned by their sudden appearance, we both sat in complete silence. But just a minute later Beatrice flew back out from the laurel and straight into the vine ... followed by an irate Auntie B ... with the broom in hand.

'So much for scarecrows,' I laughed.

As the sun dropped, Auntie B and I sat outside with a cup of tea and a piece of lemon drizzle cake that she'd made earlier. We talked about the creatures we'd seen that day, including a solitary Red Admiral butterfly and of course the close encounter with the majestic ravens. Just before retreating inside, we were joined by a large bat, which circled the house like a 400-metre runner. I can't say for certain, but it was probably a woodland bat called a noctule.

***

Some sad news

Now, before I tell you about the rest of our garden family, I have to give you some sad news: The robin who kept me company when I was cutting-up logs, in the woods at the top of my garden, was found dead by my neighbour David, and the collared doves, nesting over the front door, were unsuccessful in fledging their chicks. Also, the murderous sparrowhawk has been lurking in the hedges, and from time to time has swooped unseen across the garden, catching and killing an unwary woodpigeon or two. It's probably a female sparrowhawk, and she always leaves a massive pile of discarded pigeon feathers in her wake; often enough to stuff a small pillow. The death of our garden animals is always sad, but I'm afraid that's nature.

Now for the Happy News

The blue tits, woodpeckers, great tits and nuthatches have had families fledging the nest, and all are doing well.

Timothy Toad has made several appearances, normally after it's rained, and just the other day, Auntie Bridget found him under a large rock. After a brief catch-up between the two of them, the rock was gently returned to its resting place as Timothy returned to his daytime slumber. Meet Timothy in *Little Stories for Littler People*.

'Keep up the good work eating all those slugs, Timothy. See you again soon,' said Auntie B as she crept away.

Some annoying news

We may only see Timothy occasionally, but Miss Jackdaw now returns *five hundred times a day* with her rabble-rousing brothers and sisters to constantly raid all three of Auntie B's coconut

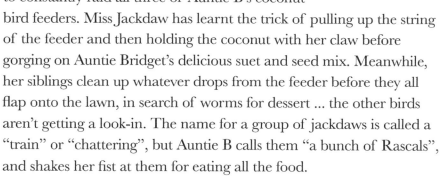

bird feeders. Miss Jackdaw has learnt the trick of pulling up the string of the feeder and then holding the coconut with her claw before gorging on Auntie Bridget's delicious suet and seed mix. Meanwhile, her siblings clean up whatever drops from the feeder before they all flap onto the lawn, in search of worms for dessert ... the other birds aren't getting a look-in. The name for a group of jackdaws is called a "train" or "chattering", but Auntie B calls them "a bunch of Rascals", and shakes her fist at them for eating all the food.

Talking of Auntie Bridget's suet and seed mix, Mr Magpie is still getting frustrated with the coconut feeders, but only yesterday he repeatedly pecked the patio doors, either in the hope of an invitation to lunch or trying to find hiding spiders to eat. In any case, he was refused entry by Auntie B, who had to shoo him away, with a rolled-up newspaper.

"Wherefore art thou Gloria?"

Now, I'm not going to fib to you and say I've seen Gloria Grass Snake this year because I haven't. Not only that, but I've not seen any snakes in our garden, and that's a great sorrow for me - if not for Auntie B, who's frightened of seeing worms, let alone snakes. All three of our native snakes are under great threat from losing their homes and being eaten, so we all need to give them a helping hand when we can. I can only hope Gloria and her friends and family are tucking themselves up for winter in some cosy leaf pile or compost heap along with the scarce hedgehogs.

The last signs of summer

The nights are getting longer as the days shorten, and it seems to have rained for weeks. In the first days of October, the last cries of summer could still be heard over the hills as birds called a *house martin* performed group acrobatics in preparation for travelling on holiday to southern Africa. And the occasional shiny enamelled, southern hawker dragonfly, with its beautiful mosaic body, was still flitting about in search of an easy insect lunch. Just last week, one of them almost landed on my nose as it looked me squarely in the eye, no more than forty centimetres away from my face.

Although I haven't seen any hornets recently, small solitary bumblebees are still visiting our garden flowers in preparation for finding a hole to sleep in, over winter.

Now, in my first letter, I promised you another hornet fact. Well, here it is: Male European hornets don't sting. And, if you happen to see a hornet, or wasp for that matter, flying about, it will almost certainly be a female. The males are pretty lazy and, almost all the time, stay tucked up in the nest. Sounds a little like me!

***

At the beginning of this letter, I mentioned not being able to go evening fishing for *Esox Lucius*. But a few weeks ago, I had an unusual night meeting with a rare garden visitor. In fact, I've never actually seen this animal in our garden before, so here's what happened.

Was it a stripy Zebra I saw the other night?

Evening and night time activity has seen the usual animals visiting, with foxes regularly making appearances, whilst the tawny owls have been heard but not seen.

Each night, come rain or moonshine, I take Holly Dog out for her final walk of the day, and this always takes us around the back garden. Now Holly Dog is a bit of a scaredy-cat, or should I say "scaredy-dog", when it comes to going into the woods at night, and two weeks ago she had good cause to be frightened.

It was around eleven o'clock in the evening, and the back lawn was well lit by a full, harvest moon. There was no colour, but every garden feature was shining silvery bright and moon-shadows were cast across the grass. I walked up to the small wooded area at the top of the garden, whilst Holly Dog stayed below in the moonlight as if to say:

'You're crazy going up there at this time of night.'

As ever, I shone my head-torch into the high branches of the trees, in the hope of seeing the reflected beam from the large "headlight" eyes of the noisy tawny owls, but as usual, they were too well hidden. It was then I heard a heavy and unusually loud rustling, coming from the compost heap. But, from where I was standing, I couldn't see what was breaking the silence.

In one of my previous letters, I said I'd found signs of one our largest carnivores coming into the garden, and, as I slowly crept around a log pile, my head-torch revealed the stripy bear-like creature, rummaging deep in the grass cuttings.

Can you guess what stripy creature it was? A zebra, maybe? Well, actually, this was a young adult badger, *not a zebra*, digging with his or her hugely powerful front paws. Badgers have a great sense of smell and they are quite capable of detecting bugs and beetles buried up to half a metre under the compost. But their eyesight isn't great, so it didn't notice my stealthy approach. Suddenly the digging stopped and, the badger turned its head towards me. At that moment the *"furry bear"* gave out a quick snort before deciding, with great bluster and a little low-pitched growling, to hastily retreat into the nearby bushes. Badgers are strong creatures and have a powerful bite. They panic when surprised or cornered, so they're best left alone. Our new visitor disappeared, leaving a trail of shaking bushes, and no proper "goodbye".

My heart was still pounding from this exciting encounter as I walked back down to the seated Holly Dog, and she looked at me as if to say ...

"I told you so; crazy going up there. It's not *your* garden at night" ... and she's quite right.

We share this world; we don't own it.

Maddie and Me

As there have been lots of night-time goings-on, I decided to set up an old field trap camera that Auntie Bridget bought for me some years ago. The camera takes a short video whenever an animal wanders past at night.

Now, as *you* weren't around to help me set up the camera, Auntie B and I asked Maddie, who is our granddaughter and about the same age as you are, to lend me a hand. In the garden, we made up a campfire in our old brazier, which is a kind of metal dustbin, and placed around it some comfy chairs and cosy blankets. All three of us enjoyed its warmth and welcoming glow as the dark cloak of early evening fell around us. Just before the flames of the fire settled down to a more peaceful rest, we barbequed sausages and beef burgers by candlelight, and, planned our mini night-time photographic garden adventure.

After the embers of the fire died back a little, Maddie and I set out with the illuminated head-torch and the camera to capture some overnight pictures of our garden wildlife.

We peered into bushes and trees as we made our way up the little paths to the woods, where I'd seen the badger. Maddie strapped the video camera to a tree trunk and switched it on, and I checked it was working.

We made our way back down to the warm brazier, where Auntie B had prepared hot chocolate and barbequed marshmallows. As we sat under the blankets, I recalled the story of our little fox, OLB, to Maddie and Auntie B. It bought back such happy memories, in the glow and snug warmth of the fire.

Colour me in!

As the night started to chill, the trees awoke to a gentle autumn breeze, and their jangling leaves told us it was time for bed.

Early the next morning, Maddie and I retrieved the camera from the woods and looked at the captured videos. The images revealed we had been visited by at least one fox, with a very bushy tail, a night bird that might have been a tawny owl, and our dozy rat, which I'd woken up in the bird feeder with a poke of my finger a few months earlier.

Maddie and I didn't catch any pictures of deer on the camera, and I've not seen them in the garden this year, but they have visited. Our neighbour David has found deer droppings in his garden, and his flowers have been eaten by them.

Later that morning, Maddie and I set about cutting up some owl pellets to investigate what bones we could find. It was great fun. As you may remember, owls choke-up the remains of food they can't digest, such as feathers, bones and fur. We found bones from birds and mice but, I'm glad to say these bones didn't come from our resident rodent, Molly.

Molly Mouse

Speaking of which, Molly Mouse and Auntie B are still best exercise buddies and have moved on from Pilates to some strange physical activity called "Cardio" ... it's all very peculiar to me. We think Molly may have had a family as Auntie Bridget didn't see her for a while. But then, in August Molly popped up, going backwards and forwards

Colour me in!

206

across the balcony, collecting more food than she could have possibly eaten, and it was quite early in the year for her to start hoarding or 'to cache' food for winter. I believe Molly may live only in Auntie B's imagination as I've yet to see her. But Auntie Bridget did find a cache of acorns under her car bonnet today, so maybe Molly's been hitching a ride into Haslemere for a flat white after exercise class.

And finally ... The Beavers

Now, as we come to a close, you may remember the very first letter I sent, in which I apologised for not being able to enter a float in the Hythe Venetian Fete, I wrote about an adventure to find a pair of beavers. So it seems perfect to end where we started.

Four weeks ago, I went fishing on the river Wey with my friend Matt from the National Trust. He is involved with introducing the beavers to the location just south of Black Down, where I had my first adventure. You may remember I didn't find the beavers but ended up discovering the beautiful roebuck antlers. Well, Matt told me that, due to this nasty virus, the arrival of our beavers has been delayed and that means as I write, today, they are still not here. I'm going to have to wait before I, once more, set out on another adventure to find these wild creatures, absent from our local world for hundreds of years. So, after their arrival, maybe together we could go on an expedition to find them. How does that sound?

I really hope you have enjoyed these letters and stories, all of which were based on my own experiences. It's been such a shame we haven't been able to meet up this year, due to this horrible virus, but in the meantime feel free to write to me with your own adventure stories. I may not be able to reply, but you never know.

And remember all of the animals mentioned in my stories, except, possibly the beavers, either live or visit close to where you live.

Keep looking, and you will discover ... Discover, and you will keep looking!

Well, I think it's time for me to take Holly Dog out for her last walk of the evening, and she's getting impatient for her bedtime biscuit. Oh, I almost forgot to tell you; she will be fifteen years old tomorrow, so I'll give her your love and congratulations in the morning.

Have a lovely Christmas.

My very best regards,
Old Uncle Steve

P.S. I've received a letter from a family saying that some of you may have younger brothers and sisters. And I have been asked to write a couple of short letters to them. You might like to read these stories out loud to your siblings.

You can find the stories of Timothy Toad and Edward in the Little Stories for Littler People section of this book – October Letters.

One of Gloria's "Mates"

Auntie B's "Scareblackbird"

DAYTIME FUN ACTIVITY

Owl Pellet Dissection – (Pellets available from the Suffolk Owl Sanctuary(SOS))

WHAT IS AN OWL PELLET?
Owls are carnivores, which mean they only eat meat. They catch mice, small rats, voles, frogs, insects, and sometimes small birds and even fish! Their prey is often eaten whole and the "meaty" bits get digested but the hard bones, fur and feathers get "coughed" up, rather than "pooed" out. These bundles of regurgitated bones and fur are called "pellets", and are usually soft, dry and don't smell as they haven't passed through the bird.

WHY LOOK AT OWL PELLETS?
Owls are near the top of the "food chain", but on occasions they are, themselves, prey for other Birds of Prey, such as Goshawks. Owl pellets contain all of the bones and feathers of their food, so by cutting open these pellets we can see exactly what they have eaten and therefore which animals are in the surrounding countryside.

Owls are very often found at the top of their particular food chain and we know that they have a very significant part to play ecologically, but we still have a long way to go before we know their exact role and just how vital it is. Studying an Owl's pellets can provide us with important information about all sorts of aspects such as prey and habitat.

WHAT YOU MIGHT FIND INSIDE
Often the skulls, jaws and other bones are both complete and identifiable. By separating out the different bones (and feathers), and with the help of a guide sheet, we can list the animals eaten and which the individual owl preferred or which was easiest and most numerous to find.

HOW TO DISSECT YOUR OWL PELLET

Write your name and the date on a clean piece of card
- Using the tweezers and a cocktail stick, tease the pellets apart
- With the tweezers, carefully remove anything you find, clean it up and dry it on a paper towel
- Match each item you remove with the SOS Bone Identification Chart
- Stick the items you have found on to your clean piece of card, carefully labelling each part as you do so.
- Remember to write the name of the prey on the card, once you are sure what it is - you may need more than one piece of card, if you think you have found more than one type of prey!

... AND FINALLY; A BLACK DOWN BEAVER!

After countless times of trying to photograph these illusive creatures, this was the best I could manage. Can you see the beaver's fur and slightly red eye between the two tree trunks?

.... BRINGING YOU UP-TO-DATE

In mid-March 2021, a pair of beavers was released into the safe keeping of a 37 acre site on the side of Black Down. I've been asked not to reveal the exact location.

As a "keystone*" species, it is hoped the beavers presence will help to produce a more diverse natural, local environment for many years to come. And, as a breeding pair, their offspring may help to populate other such project enclaves.

The raven population continues to grow slowly in our region, with their iconic cry being heard across the hills and woodland. In March 2021, a pair of these juvenile marauders visited the high tops of the pine trees in our garden, stealing an egg from one of our crows' nests. The crows were not pleased and escorted the ravens off the premise to a very distant pine tree.

Otter tracks have been identified on the bank of the southern branch of the river Wey through February, and I've been asked to set up a camera trap, if possible, to catch their activity.

Just the other day, I went back to the old mill pond, which is a little downstream from our Esox Lucius night time adventure story. I happened to meet the farmer who looks after the pond and I told him about Esox. His eyes lit-up as he pulled out his mobile phone. After scrolling through some of his pictures for a minute or two he stopped, and with a smile passed me the phone ... There it was, a photo of Esox;

not six kilograms, but closer to sixteen; a true monster. It's exciting to think that Esox Lucius still lurks in the hidden depths of the tiny river Lod.

Esox Lucius was safely returned to the water to haunt the river Lod once more. (Photo taken by Andrew Loughan)

Holly Dog still sits on "her" little sofa, under the tall lamp next to me, and I often read aloud to her the letters I've written for you, in search of her approval. She is into her seventeenth year, which is pretty old for a Labrador. We still walk in the local hills, lakes and rivers each day, albeit a little more slowly than once we did. But, her walking "Bestie", Charlie, a working cocker spaniel, has unfortunately passed away recently. Charlie was a big part of Laura's family, and mine. His excitable personality will be sadly missed by us all. As you may know, Laura is the illustrator of this book.

"You, I, Holly Dog and Charlie will forever walk together in this, our beautiful land."

A Keystone species is one that has a positive and pivotal effect on their environment, either directly or indirectly, without which the ecosystem would be degraded.

Do you have a pet or favourite animal you could draw here?

LITTLE STORIES FOR
THE LITTLER PEOPLE

Timothy was well camouflaged on the pebbles

The October Letters – Part 1:
"The Tale of Timothy Toad"

"The bristly badger picked Timothy up and popped Timothy into his bristly, badger-sized mouth"

To The Family

Date: Early October.

Hello,
Auntie Bridget and I were clearing away some leaves in our garden, and we found a big toad. It got me thinking about writing a story just for you. So here it is.

Camilla's Story – Timothy Toad
Timothy Toad lived in a deep, dark, damp drain.

Timothy would like to have been called Tim or Timmy by his friends, but Timothy didn't have any friends.

So Timothy was just called ...Timothy ... Timothy Toad.

Timothy was born in a dirty drainage ditch, very near to his deep, dark, damp drain.

Timothy had a mummy, daddy, brothers and sisters, but he never saw them.

Timothy lived quite alone and he didn't like it.

Timothy also didn't like going out in the daylight because he thought he looked ugly.

The sunlight gave Timothy sore skin, and once a slippery snake tried to eat him.

So, Timothy only left his deep, dark, damp drain at night.

Timothy wanted adventure in his life as much as he wanted a friend.

Late one evening, Timothy set off from his deep, dark, damp drain to find the friend he longed for.

First, Timothy met a slippery, slimy, slug, munching on a dandelion leaf.

"Er...Um," Timothy cleared his throat. "Excuse me, but I wondered if you would be my friend?" Timothy asked.

The slippery slimy slug didn't reply and continued to eat the dandelion leaf.

"Um, Um," Timothy tried again to get the attention of the slippery, slimy slug. "Excu..." Timothy stopped.

Suddenly, Timothy felt rather hungry as he looked at the slippery, slimy slug.

Timothy opened his huge mouth; stuck out his sticky tongue and gobbled up the slippery, slimy slug.

"Not a great start to finding a best friend," Timothy thought.

Timothy moved on.

Next, Timothy came across a hairy hedgehog, out for a night-time stroll.

"Excuse me, but would you be my friend?" Timothy asked the hairy hedgehog, politely.

"I haven't got time to talk to you," said the hairy hedgehog, and with that the hairy hedgehog pushed passed, giving Timothy a nasty prod with one of his sharp spikes.

"That hurt," Timothy thought. "The hairy hedgehog is not my friend."

Timothy moved on.

Into the darkness, Timothy trudged on until he met a bristly badger.

Timothy tugged the tail of the bristly badger.

The bristly badger turned and looked at Timothy.

"And who are you?" asked the bristly badger.

"I'm Timothy Toad," replied Timothy.

"I think I like toads," said the bristly badger.

"A friend at last!" Timothy thought.

The bristly badger picked Timothy up and popped Timothy into his bristly, badger-sized mouth.

"Oh dear," thought Timothy, remembering when he met the slippery snake, who tried to eat him.

The bristly badger had a big mouth with big teeth, and Timothy was rolled around and around by the bristly badger's big tongue.

Then, without warning, the bristly badger spat Timothy out of his mouth and onto the ground.

"I remember now, I don't like toads. They taste horrible," said the bristly badger.

With that, the bristly badger walked off without even saying "Goodbye."

"How rude," Timothy thought.

Then Timothy heard a friendly sounding voice coming from a nearby bush.

"Are you okay?" said the friendly voice. "Do you need a friend to help you?"

"Yes, please," said Timothy.

"What is your name?" asked Timothy

"Tamsin Toad, but you can call me Tammy if you want," the friendly voice replied. "What's your name?"

"That's funny because my name is also Toad ... Timothy Toad. But if we are friends, you can call me Timmy Toad," said Timothy.

"A FRIEND AT LAST," Timothy whispered to himself.

The two friends met each other every night after that, and often shared a worm or two, next to the dirty drainage ditch.

Soon there was the sound of baby toads, croaking and hopping out of the dirty drainage ditch.

Now, maybe, just maybe, those tiny toads found their own homes in a deep dark damp drain, somewhere near where you live. Keep your eyes peeled!

I hope you enjoyed this story, which I have written especially for you.

All my love
Great, Old Uncle Steve

"This baby "toadlet" (or froglet!) was about to leave my little pond ... Could it be one of Timothy's offspring?"

The October Letters – Part 2: "Edward and His Friends"

"Edward said "Goodbye" to all his friends"

To The Family

Date: Late October.

Hello again,

I understand you enjoyed the last letter and story I sent to you about Timothy Toad. So, I thought you might like to read about Edward and his friends. And, just like Edward, this story has a "Twist in the *Tail*". I hope you enjoy it ... Oh, *what creature do you think Edward is – Dog or cat maybe?*

Violet's Story – Edward and his friends

Edward lived in a big shed with his friends.

Edward was very young.

Edward enjoyed playing with his friends in the straw.

Edward had special friends; Victoria Vole and Simon Shrew.

Edward was also friends with Roger Rat, but Roger Rat was always getting into trouble.

Roger Rat would steal food from the other animals and blamed it on Edward.

Roger Rat sometimes played tricks on Simon Shrew and blamed them on Edward.

Edward didn't like that very much.

Edward had a best friend called Malcolm Mouse.

Edward's mummy and daddy were frightened by Malcolm Mouse because Malcolm Mouse squeaked a lot.

Malcolm Mouse and Edward would play together in the straw all day if they could.

But Edward, Malcolm, Victoria, Simon, and of course Roger had to go to school:

Circus school!

Victoria Vole learned to walk on a tightrope of hemp twine.

Simon Shrew learnt to swing on a trapeze of grass stalks.

Malcolm Mouse learnt to juggle five grains of wheat, *all at the same time.*

Roger Rat learned ... how to play truant from school!

But Edward couldn't join in because the teacher said he was TOO BIG.

Edward was very sad.

Edward could wiggle his long nose better than Simon Shrew.

Edward could wiggle his long tail and big ears better than Malcolm Mouse or even Roger Rat, when he was at school.

Edward could stand on his two back legs ... Even Victoria Vole couldn't do that.

"You're just TOO BIG, Edward," said his teacher, Miss Harriet House Mouse.

"You're just TOO BIG, Edward," said Edward's mummy and daddy.

"I'll show them I'm not TOO BIG," said Edward.

Edward tried to squeeze into a matchbox.

But Edward was just TOO BIG.

Edward tried squeezing though Simon Shrew's front door.

But Edward was just TOO BIG.

Edward tried to balance on Victoria Vole's tightrope ... but it broke.

But Edward was just TOO BIG.

Every day Edward got BIGGER, and all his friends seemed to get smaller.

Edward got older, and he didn't realise why he was so different from all his friends.

Children, do you know why Edward was so different from his friends?

Well, Edward decided to run away and find another circus school.

Edward packed his "trunk" with his favourite toys.

Edward said "Goodbye" to all his friends.

Edward couldn't find another circus school, but Edward did find a circus.

"Hello," said the Ringmaster of the circus.

"Hello Sir," said Edward, politely. "Could I join your circus?"

"We don't usually have animals like you in our circus," said the Ringmaster.

"Oh dear," said Edward "But I can be very helpful."

"What can you do? "Asked the Ringmaster.

"I can lift heavy things; I can juggle a ball on my long wiggly nose; I can wiggle my big ears, and I can stand on my back legs," said Edward helpfully.

"Well," said the Ringmaster. "My juggler is ill for our show tonight

... would you take her place?"

"I would love to," Edward said excitedly.

At the show that night, Edward juggled a ball on his nose; wiggled his large ears, and stood on his back legs. He even helped move things around and take the circus tent down.

Everybody clapped and cheered.

"We want Edward ... We want Edward!" they shouted.

The Ringmaster was so pleased.

"Edward, you were brilliant," the Ringmaster said.

"Edward, you are so strong," said the Clown.

"Edward, you have great wiggly ears," said the Candyfloss Seller.

"Edward, you have a great wiggly nose," said the Trapeze Artist.

"Edward, you have a great wiggly, curly tail," said the Juggler.

Edward smiled and said, "I'm not bad for a big mouse, or a big vole, or a big shrew, or whatever animal I am."

Well, Kids, do you know what animal Edward is; a rat, a mouse; maybe a vole?

The Ringmaster laughed and laughed and laughed.

"You are so funny, Edward," said the Ringmaster, still laughing.

"And answer me this, Edward ... What's your second name ... Smith, Jones, Gairdner?" asked the Ringmaster.

"No, my second name isn't Smith or Jones or even Gairdner .... *My name is Edward ... Edward <u>Elephant!</u>*"

***

Well, did you guess what animal Edward was? I hope you enjoyed your special story and maybe you could draw a picture of Edward for me. See you soon.

My Kindest Regards,
Old Uncle Steve

PS. I thought you might like three special activities to do with the grownups. So, find out how to hunt for bugs, give them a home, just like yours, and how to grow your own bird seed for Auntie B's 'Seed & Suet Mix' in the "Activities to do in the Garden for the Little Ones" section of this book.

Drawn by Jemima Gairdner (age 10)

ACTIVITIES TO DO IN THE GARDEN FOR THE LITTLE ONES

It's always amazing to see just how many different types of bug, beetle and birds are living in our gardens and parks. So, here are two activities you can do. For the Bug Hunt you may need a garden but for the 'Bee and Bird Cafe' you only need a balcony.

So there is a simple way to find out who is out there.

THE BUG TRAP (YOU MAY NEED PERMISSION TO DO THIS)
What you'll need:
• Wide topped jam jar or tin, which should be about 5cm or more deep.
• Small rock to fit inside the jar.
• Trowel or old spoon for digging a "jar sized" hole.
• A marker or flag to identify where the jar is located.
• Pen/pencil and paper.
• Phone/camera.

How to set your Bug trap
• Find a spot in your garden, which is shaded and preferably has leaf-litter and old twigs lying around.
• Temporarily, clear away the litter to enable a hole to be dug that's large enough to accept the jar, so the top of the lip of the jar is level with the ground.
• Now place the rock at the bottom of the jar*.
• Level out the soil around the top of the jar and place two or three twigs across the top of the jar, leaving plenty of gaps.
• Now cover the surrounding ground and jar with a thin layer of leaf-litter, and mark the jar location with the flag or marker.

226

Leave for no longer than two days (normally just 24 hours) and then go back and reveal what you've caught before releasing the captives. If you can, take a photo of the beetles and bugs for identification on line or in a reference book. Use the pencil and paper to record how many of each species you find. Replant the jar and repeat the above to build up a database of bugs in your garden and when they were caught.

*If it rains whilst you are away from your Bug Trap be sure to release the captives straight away. The stone will provide a temporary "island" for them to climb onto. If you are not using the trap you can leave it in place only if you secure the jar top back on the jar, ready for the next experiment.

GROW YOUR OWN SUNFLOWERS ON A BALCONY OR GARDEN AND GATHER THE SEEDS FOR THE BIRDS.

It's so simple and great fun to grow your own Sunflower seeds for your "Auntie B's Magic Suet & Seed Mix", and here is how you do it.

What you'll need:
• A finger!
• A small flower pot; or paper cup; or jam jar (minimum 12cms high by 12cms diameter).
• Two or three larger flower pots, or old saucepans; or metal paper bins (minimum 20cm high by 15cm diameter).
• Garden compost or just soil – enough to fill your pots.
• Three to six black sunflower seeds (some may not grow) from Auntie B's seed mix (these are the largest of the seeds in the bird seed mix and are the shape of a spearhead)
• Labels to mark the pots.

What to do

- Soak your black sunflower seeds in a glass of water overnight and use seeds that sink to the bottom.
- Fill each little pot to the top with compost or soil.
- Poke three holes in the compost/soil with your finger to a depth of about 3cms.
- Place a black sunflower seed into each hole and cover with the compost/soil.
- Water well without water-logging each pot. Keep moist at all times. Place in a sunny spot, say on a windowsill.
- After two weeks you should see green shoots poking out of the compost.
- When they outgrow the little pot it's time to re-pot each sunflower into its own larger pot and place outside (on your balcony or garden) in the sunniest spot.
- Keep them moist and watch them grow and flower over the following months.
- Watch out for all the bees that visit your flowers and see how many different species of bee turn up.
- When the flowers have died back and gone completely brown, cut off the flower head and keep in a dry and airy place until the seed become loose, like a wobbly tooth.
- Pick or brush out the seeds from the dry flower head.
- Use all of the seeds for your 'Auntie B's Magic Mix' all winter, but remember to keep some of your seeds for next year's planting.

BUG AND BEE HOUSE

You can make a bug and bee house as simple as you like. So I'm going to describe to you the simplest "home"

What you'll need:
- Any tin or plastic cup (recycled or repurposed)
- A range of different widths of sticks, but enough to fill the tin or cup when stood up in the container. Even better, Bamboo Cane.
- A small handful of dried leaves (optional)
- String.
- That's it!

What to do:
- Fill the tin or cup with just a few centimetres of the dried leaf litter.
- Break the twigs to a length which is just shorter than the depth of the cup or tin. If you were lucky enough to find a bamboo cane, cut[*] it into several lengths to the same length as the broken twigs.
- Check the twigs and/or bamboo fit fairly tightly into the tin or cup, but, so they don't poke out, when they are lying lengthways in the tin, like long sausages in a tin.
- Take them back out of the tin or cup and lie all together around the stick bunch with the string. Make sure the sticks and/or bamboo are level with each other at one end.
- Push the stick/bamboo bundle back into the cup/tin so the level end of the bunch is just in line with the open end of the cup/tin.
- If the bundle is still a little loose in the cup/tin don't worry, just gently push in a small stick or two between the bundle and the cup/tin until the bundle is secure.

- Now place the cup or tin on its side in a cool shaded place in your garden or on your balcony.
- You can leave it there for a year or longer and just keep going back to see who has moved in.

Always get an adult to cut bamboo and never try to snap it as the bamboo might splinter and you will never get a smooth end.

YOUR LETTER TO ME

Maybe you would like to write your own story and letter to send to me.
If so, write your letter below for safe keeping and send me a copy to:

Stephen Frye   Date:

Haslewood House, Haslemere

GU27 2LF

Dear Uncle Steve

....

....

....

....

....

....

....

....

....

....

Kind Regards

Draw a picture here

THE QUIZ ANSWER SECTION

ANSWERS - BLACK DOWN ACTIVITIES

Beaver facts, which one Beaver fact is TRUE?

- Baby beavers, called kits, can't swim until they are, at least three weeks old ... *False, they can swim after just a day. Their eyes are open from birth.*
- The tail of a beaver shrinks in winter ... **True, their tail is made of muscle and fat. The fat is stored in the tail, in autumn, and used in winter, hence it shrinks in size.**
- Beavers mainly eat leaves, roots, bark and plants, but in very cold winters they also eat fish and fresh water mussels for fat and protein ... *False, beavers are herbivores and don't eat meat.*
- Generally, the natural colour of a beaver's teeth is light grey ... *False, their teeth are coloured orange.*
- Beavers live and have their families inside their river dams for protection ... *False, their homes, called lodges, are made from branches, mud and moss on the waters' edge of river, ponds and stick-islands, not inside their dams.*

Mysterious Black Down

See if you can complete the Black Down crossword puzzle below - The answers are at the back of this book

Created using the Crossword Maker on TheTeachersCorner.net

Across

2. What did I tip out of my rucksack? (**cagoule**)
4. Which animals live in homes called 'lodges'? (**beavers**)
7. What breed of dog is Holly dog? (**labrador**)
8. What was food for hungry mice? (**bilberries**)

Down

1. What had escaped from a nearby farm? (**wildboar**)
3. Where do I live? (**haslemere**)
5. What fell into my eye? (**snowflakes**)
6. On Black Down, what did Holly dog bark at in the grass? (**antlers**)

232

THE ROBIN'S STORY ACTIVITIES – ANSWERS

Which TWO of the following statements are TRUE?
- When robins have become adults they don't moult in summer ... *False, Robins moult after the breeding season in late summer. They are rarely seen at this time.*
- Robins never migrate overseas ... *False, some young male robins do fly over to mainland Europe even going as far as southern Europe, but most stay within a few kilometres from where they are fledged.*
- Robins are territorial and will fight each other to the death if need be ... **True. In particular, males will kill each other over territories.**
- Robins will feed other fledglings, such as song thrushes and were once thought to be members of the thrush family ... **True. Robins, albeit not alone in doing this, will sometimes feed other species fledglings and were believed to be members the thrush family before reclassification as "flycatchers".**
- Robins have only one brood, or family, a year and mate with the same partner for life ... *False, robins will often have two or more broods a year and often with different partners in the same year.*

SCARY NIGHTS ACTIVITIES – ANSWERS

Which ONE of the Barn Owl fact below is TRUE

- Ideally, a pair of barn owls, including feeding their family, will catch up to 2000 prey animals a year ... *False, actually a successful pair will catch double that amount.*
- Barn owls digest all the bones and fur of their prey ... *False, They can't digest bones and fur*
- Barn owls don't pooh, they just "squirt out" a white, runny liquid.... **True, they don't produce solid faeces, as such; rather, they choke-up, or "cast" what they can't digest in the form of hard, dry pellets.**
- Barn owls have fantastic night vision and hunt mainly by sight ... *False, well, actually they do have great eyesight, many times better than ours, but they hunt mainly by sound and have the best hearing of any land animal tested (1981).*
- Due to their small beaks and mouths, barn owls have to tear apart their dinner before swallowing it ... *False, they almost always eat their prey whole. (Thanks to the Barn Owl Trust for this information)*

Scary Winter Nights

Using the stories to help you, complete the crossword puzzle below

Created using the Crossword Maker on TheTeachersCorner.net

Across

2. What were the two 'flying' predators called? (**barnowl**)
4. What fell into the dark pool of water? (**headtorch**)
5. Where did I fish as a boy? (**ghostlake**)
6. What is the name of the little river where Esox lived? (**lod**)
7. Who was The Beast from The Deep? (**esoxlucius**)

Down

1. What shone in the sky at night? (**wolfmoon**)
3. What did we throw behind the hedge at Ghost Lake? (**tackleboxes**)
5. What sound came from 'Grave' Island? (**groaning**)

GARDEN GUEST ACTIVITIES - ANSWERS

Garden guests – Fact File. Which ONE of these statements is FALSE?

- Grass snakes are Britain's largest reptile and lay eggs. However, adders give birth to LIVE young - *True, females can reach 120 cm long, and lay eggs, unlike adders.*
- Unlike the native deer of Britain, Muntjac Deer breed (rut) all year round *– True, they have no set breeding season. It's said that many of the UK population of Muntjac deer escaped or were released from Woburn Park, Bedfordshire.*
- Unfortunately, hedgehogs can't swim and often drown if they stumble into ponds. **– False, They are quite good swimmers and normally only drown if they can't get out. So, if you have a garden pond always make sure there is a place for them to climb out.**
- Female sparrowhawks are up to twice the weight of males. *– True, Females can be 25% larger and twice the weight. They are less agile avian hunters than the males, but can catch larger bird prey, such as woodpigeons.*
- Brown rats can grow to half a metre in length from nose to tail tip, and are more often "right-handed". *– True, and research shows that over 70% of them are right-handed. (PMID: 14602540 DOI: 10.1080/00207450390249258 – Mustafa Guven).*
- Tawny Owls are quite capable of wading in ponds and catching fish *– True, and they will also catch frogs and other amphibians. (Thanks to the Owl Trust)*
- A Greater Spotted Woodpecker can peck up to 20 times a second. *– True, and it's believed they can peck, or "drum" over 11,000 times a day.*

*The "tweety" Song Thrush, collecting worms for
his recently hatched chicks*

"Each morning, before dawn, I'm woken by an annoyingly
noisy and tweety Song Thrush, who, it would seem, feels
the need to wake everybody up before the sun rises."

*A magnificent Roebuck with velvet-covered
four-pronged antlers*

" ... he was adorned with a pair of magnificent antlers,
which he would use to fight other stags in the
"rutting", or "breeding" season."

THE FOX AND THE FRIENDSHIP ACTIVITIES - THE ANSWERS

Our Little Boy – games; True or false
- Red Foxes' front paws each have five digits (or toes), like us. However, they have only four on their hind, or back paws – **True, they have dewclaws only on their front paws, which is similar to most dogs.**
- Foxes have a maximum speed of 25mph – *False, just over 30mph is considered their top speed.*
- Female foxes, called vixens, normally have two families a year – *False, they reproduce once a year.*
- Foxes live in homes called lodges. – *False, they live in dens or earths.*
- Red Foxes aren't found in Australia – *False, they were introduced in 19 Century.*

The Fox and the Friendship
See if you can unscramble the words from the story below

Created on TheTeachersCorner.net Scramble Maker

1.	lrLuea egedH	Laurel Hedge	Where did I first see the fox's head?
2.	urO Ltelti yBo	Our Little Boy	What name did we call the fox?
3.	gywnmHhaai	Highwayman	Who or what did we think the fox looked like?
4.	oBcna	Bacon	What type of meat did we first give to the fox?
5.	uaSassge	Sausages	What else did we feed to the fox?
6.	llyoH goD	Holly Dog	Who got annoyed with the fox?
7.	inG Tapr	Gin Trap	What did the fox get caught in?
8.	PSACR	RSPCA	Who gave us a cage?
9.	Reo eDer	Roe Deer	What type of animal became friends with the fox?

ANIMALS BEHAVING BADLY & HOUSE GUEST ACTIVITIES - THE ANSWERS

Raven – Which statement is TRUE?
- Ravens lay their eggs in April .... *False; they lay their eggs in February. Ravens are one of the earliest birds to lay in the year.*
- Adult ravens have a wingspan of just under one metre ... *False; their wingspan is up to one and a half metres; longer than even a buzzard.*
- Ravens can fly upside down for short distances .... **True; there are other birds around the world that can turn upside down but normally only to land or fend off other birds – Ravens do it often "just for fun" in free flight or courtship. I've seen this happening on Black Down.**
- Ravens are Raptors ... *False; they are Corvids.*
- Ravens are in the same "Bird Family" as Blackbirds, called Turdidae ... *False; blackbirds are members of the Thrush family.*

Jackdaw facts (or Fiction) – Which ONE Jackdaw statement below is FALSE?
- Jackdaws recognise individual human faces and expressions - *True, Cambridge zoologist, Auguste von Bayern showed this was the case.*
- The group or collective name for a gathering of Jackdaws is a Train, amongst other names. – *True, and another collective name is: A "clattering" of jackdaws.*
- Jackdaws can have same-gender pairings. – *True, in 1930 ornithologist Konrad Lorenz observed this behaviour in both male and female adolescent jackdaws.*
- A Jackdaw in Rheims (France) was, for a short time, made a saint for returning the Bishop's ring to the Cathedral. *False, this was mentioned in the poem by R.H. Barham, but it was never actually the case.*
- Jackdaws were once called "The Chimney Sweep" bird. **True, they were also called "The College Bird" and "Sea Crow".**

Thanks to Ian Morton of Country Life for the Barham and chimney sweep references

Blackbird facts (or fiction)? Which statement is TRUE.

- Blackbirds are members of the same family as crows, rooks, jackdaws and jays. – *False, Blackbirds may be black but they are members of the Thrush Family, along with Fieldfares, Redwings to name but two.*
- Blackbirds, like crows, can have a combination of black and white feathers. **True, very few are albinos, but both birds exhibit a condition called "Leucism", which results in combinations of white and black feathers being grown (this should not be confused with albinism, which accounts for around 10% of white coloured blackbirds). I've seen both leucistic blackbirds and crows in my garden over the years. Other animals also exhibit leucism, such as badgers. The affected feathers have no pigment.**
- All UK, male blackbirds have yellow beaks. – *False, juvenile male blackbirds have a greyish coloured beak, which may remain that colour for up to nine months. You will see male blackbirds with grey beaks in your garden throughout winter, and many youngsters may have migrated from the Continent looking for territories.*
- Iceland is the only European country to have no breeding pairs of Blackbirds. – *False, It's commonly believed that blackbirds don't breed in Iceland, but research and observations since the '90s demonstrate otherwise, especially in the south, although it is by no means common. The first sighting was seen in 1969.*
- The first blackbirds to sing each year are mature males. – *Nope, false again. It is the juvenile males that sing from late January to establish a territory. Adult males start singing in March. (Thanks to Sara Hudston – Guardian Country Diary).*

House Guests Crossword

See if you can complete the House Guests Crossword below.

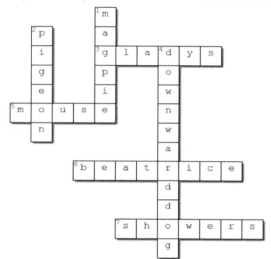

Created using the Crossword Maker on TheTeachersCorner.net

Across

3. Who used the cat flap to get into the kitchen? (**gladys**)

5. What animal did Auntie B exercise with? (**mouse**)

6. What was the name of Auntie B's Bath time Buddie (**beatrice**)

7. Where do Blackbirds prefer to wash themselves (**showers**)

Down

1. Which type of bird invited himself to lunch? (**magpie**)

2. What 'nested' in the lampshade? (**pigeon**)

4. What type of 'animal' exercise did Auntie B do? (**downwarddog**)

241

THE BEAST OF EXMOOR ACTIVITIES - THE ANSWERS

The captor in the photo is a *grass snake*, sometimes called a '*water snake*' because of its love of ponds and rivers. The Latin name for grass snakes is '*Natrix natrix*', which may come from the Latin word 'nare', to swim.

Well hidden ... close-up of the grass snake with the Bullhead fish in its mouth

Which ONE of these statements is TRUE?
- Otters have four toes on each foot – *False, they have five, but very often only four are visible in footprints. Interestingly, they also have webbed feet.*
- Otters have been spotted recently in all UK counties except for the Isle of White and Anglesey – *False, I'm pleased to say otters have been spotted throughout the country and in every county, including some towns and cities.*
- Otters have the densest (more follicles per square inch) fur of any other animal - **True, as many as half a million hairs per square inch in places. (ref; Rachel Anne Kuhn (2010).**
- Otters have fewer teeth than adult humans ... *False, 32 for human & 32 or more for otter.*
- A male otter can have a territory of up to six miles of river – *False. His territory can be in excess of twelve miles.*

The Beast of Exmoor Crossword

Can you fill in the Crossword Quiz below?

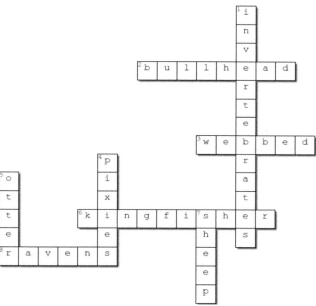

Created using the Crossword Maker on TheTeachersCorner.net

Across

2. Which fish did God accidently step on? (**bullhead**)
3. What feet did the creature have that sat next to me? (**webbed**)
6. What brightly coloured bird flew along the river? (**kingfisher**)
8. Which birds live in The Tower of London? (**ravens**)

Down

1. What do we call the minute creatures that don't have bones? (**invertebrates**)
4. Which mythical creatures couldn't enter Heaven or Hell? (**pixies**)
5. Which animal sat on the damhead? (**otter**)
7. Which animal went missing in the night? (**sheep**)

ANSWERS – RIVER WEY ACTIVITIES

Which ONE of the following statements is FALSE?
- Stoats are related to badgers – *True, they are both members of the Mustelidae family, or mustelid as they are commonly known.*
- Stoats can have white coats in winter – *True, but only in colder parts of the country. The tips of their tails stay blackish in colour throughout the year.*
- Stoats normally have two litters (families of babies) per year; one in early spring and the other in mid-autumn – **FALSE, they only have one litter, in spring, but mate in summer of the previous year. Their gestation period can be up to 300 days long.**
- Stoats bounce up and down whenever they run about. However, weasels don't bounce when they run. *True*
- Stoats are up to three times bigger than weasels. *True. Weasels are our smallest carnivores, weighing as little as 55 grams.*

The Gairdner Family visiting *"Ghost Lake"*, along with the children's grandfather, John, and Tippa the dog

ADVENTURE LOCATION MAP
The south of England

1. Royal Military Canal (Hythe) – Home of the Venetian Fete.
2. Black Down Hill – A place of mystery & intrigue.
3. The River Wylye – The robin and friendships.
4. Saltwood & "Ghost Lake"; now known as Brockhill Country Park – Open to the public. Follow https://en.wikipedia.org/wiki/Brockhill_Country_Park.
5. The River Lod – Esox Lucius; scary winter's night.
6. Haslemere, Surrey – Garden & house guests.
7. Exmoor National Park – A place of rugged beauty, myths & legends.
8. The River Exe - "The Beast of Exmoor".
9. Central London and the River Thames.
10. The River Wey (north and south branches) – Wildlife stories.

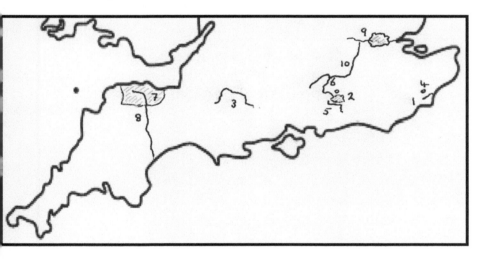

ACKNOWLEDGEMENTS

Almut Kelber (et al) – "Hornets can fly at night …" PMCID: PMC3134451

Michael Aleksiuk – "Beavers – The function of the tail as a fat storage depot".

Marilyn Shy (Reviewer) BTO – "Cross species feeding" –Robins et al

Eric Knudsen – "The hearing of Barn Owls" (1981)

Mustafa Guven) – "Rat behaviour" (PMID: 14602540)

Michel Budka – "…drumming in greater spotted woodpeckers" (PMID: 29415002)

S Evershed – "Ravens flying upside down" Nature 1930 & S. Frye observations

Lucia Izquierdo et al – "Factors associated with leucism in the common blackbird" & S. Frye observations

Iceland Review (5th May, 2020) – "Blackbirds in Iceland"

Sara Hudston (March '17) – Guardian Country Diary "Blackbird hour…" Juvenile blackbird song in January.

Rutland Wildlife Trust – "Stoats"

Thanks to Teachers' Corner for providing the games matrice.

CONSERVATION ORGANISATIONS

South East Rivers Trust

Wessex Chalk Stream & Rivers Trust

West Country Rivers Trust

Arun & Rother Rivers Trust

Wey Valley Fisheries Consultative Association

Wild Trout Trust

Surrey Wildlife Trust

Grayshott Angling Club

National Trust

Exmoor Natural History Society & The Exmoor Society

Riverfly Partnership

EA Fisheries – Thames Region

The Suffolk Owl Sanctuary

ACKNOWLEDGEMENTS

FURTHER READING

Kim Andrews – 'Exploring Nature Activity Book'.
Anita Ganeri & David Chandler – 'RSPB First Book of Minibeasts
Anita Ganeri & David Chandler – 'RSPB First Book of Birds
National Trust – 'Go Wild ....' & 'Look Who's Hiding ...' series
Derwent May - 'Life on the Wing'
Joe Shute – 'A Shadow Above' – The rise and fall of the Raven
Isabella Tree – "Wilding" The return of nature to a British farm (Knepp Experiment)
Simon Barns – "Rewild Yourself"
Jon Taylor – *www.jonnietaylor.com* & "Jonnie Taylor Countryside Walks," on Facebook.

THE AUTHOR'S PERSONAL PROFILE

Myself and my darling wife; the long-suffering "Auntie B" ... She has *asked* me to say that she's not the *nasty dragon* I've made her out to be in these letters - *but between you and me...*

Stephen Frye was educated at Dover College before graduating from Leeds University in the Dark Ages of the last Millennium. During and after a life in commerce, Stephen has been immersed in projects to regenerate and rejuvenate rivers and lakes within the Wey catchment and beyond.

Running on from his many years of Chairmanship of the Grayshott Angling Club, he was appointed as an officer of the Wey Valley Fisheries Consultancy Association and chaired the Fisheries Action Plan funding committee. This work culminated in a national award from the River Restoration Centre in 2018.

Stephen is also a co-founder of Grayswood Cricket Club, and has volunteered with Samaritans for many years, both as a listener and as a member of the prison outreach team.

The Author, as seen by Jemima Gairdner

I drew this picture of uncle steve as when I was 4 he told me a stand by his bed was a place to put he mouthe at night
I continued to belive this so when I think of him this is what I see also. The animal in his brain are to represent his love of natuere.
Jemima.